The New Scribner Music Library

DR. HOWARD HANSON

EDITOR-IN-CHIEF

———— ❖ ————

VOLUME 6

Piano for Two

Edited by

RUTH WATANABE

———— ❖ ————

CHARLES SCRIBNER'S SONS · NEW YORK

PRINTED IN THE UNITED STATES OF AMERICA
Library of Congress Catalog Card Number 72-1492

SBN 684-13107-2 (Volume 6)

SBN 684-13100-5 (Vols. 1-10 with Reference Volume, including Index)

Preface

THE piano has been called the most "lonesome" of instruments because a great part of its repertory is for solo performance. It is often pointed out that players of string instruments, of woodwind, brass, and percussion instruments, have the opportunity of playing with others in orchestras, bands, and various ensemble groups, an experience which is denied pianists.

But this is not really true. While the piano is essentially a "solo" instrument it is also a magnificent ensemble instrument, whether it appears as the solo instrument with a symphony orchestra, in chamber music, as an accompaniment for other solo instruments or voice, or as part of a piano ensemble.

There is nothing more exciting, or exacting, than a two-piano performance. There is no better way of becoming intimately acquainted with symphonic literature than through arrangements for two pianos— eight-hands or four-hands — or for piano duet. Indeed, many of us received our first introduction to the great symphonies in this manner.

However, since two pianos are not always readily available, especially in the home, the most effective and practical ensemble experience is found in the piano duet. To assist in developing this kind of ensemble technique, Dr. Watanabe has prepared a fascinating volume entitled *Piano for Two,* and consisting entirely of compositions written for piano four-hands.

The list extends from the period of Mozart, Schubert, and Beethoven, to the works of such twentieth century composers as Ernst von Dohnányi and Paul Juon. In between will be found many charming waltzes, compositions in other dance forms, and other works in a variety of styles and forms.

The volume brings not only a new musical experience to the student; it is also fun to play.

HOWARD HANSON

Introduction

TO make music with someone is one of the greatest rewards of a pianist. Not only is it an enjoyable discipline, contributing to a fine sense of ensemble and mutual cooperation among players, but a profitable pastime as well. Included in this volume are piano duets at various levels of pianistic development and encompassing various styles and forms of the classic and romantic periods. They may be played by pupil and teacher or by two students. Because the duet is the logical introduction of the young pianist to chamber music, these pieces may be used to add another dimension to a private music lesson or to a class. Moreover, most of the compositions are suitable for recital, and some of the more advanced works are of concert caliber, both technically and musically. Thus, this volume is offered as an opportunity to enjoy the pleasures of "Piano for Two."

RUTH WATANABE

For biographical information about Dr. Watanabe, see Dr. Hanson's Preface to Volume 5.

Contents

List of Titles

Waltz

Op. 66 No. 7

Secondo

Anton Arensky
(1861-1906)

Waltz
Op. 66 No. 7

Primo

Anton Arensky
(1861-1906)

Allegro non troppo

Un poco più vivo

Secondo

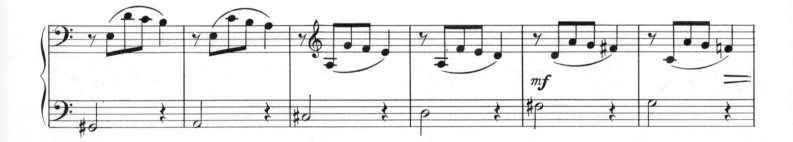

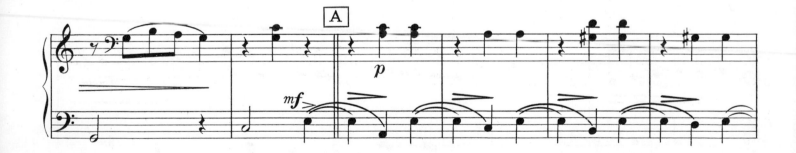

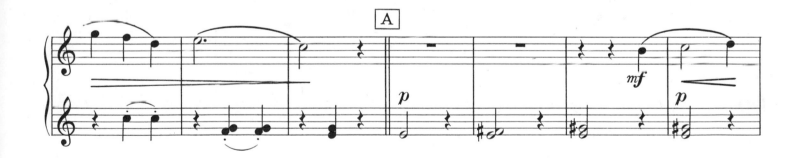

Secondo

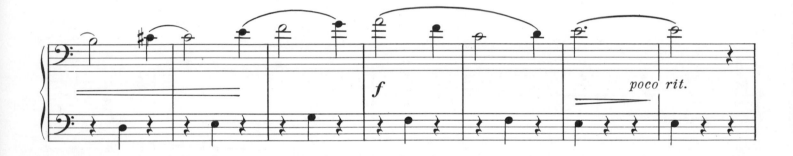

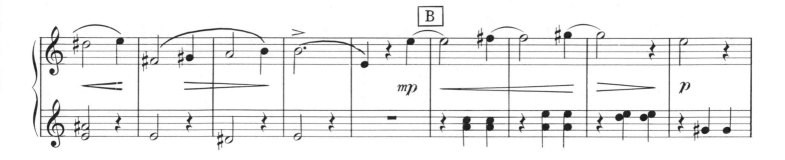

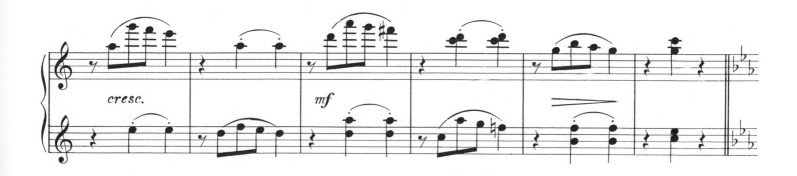

Secondo

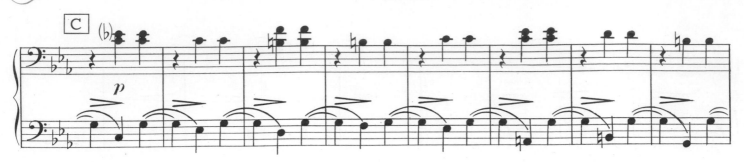

Un poco più vivo

Un poco più vivo

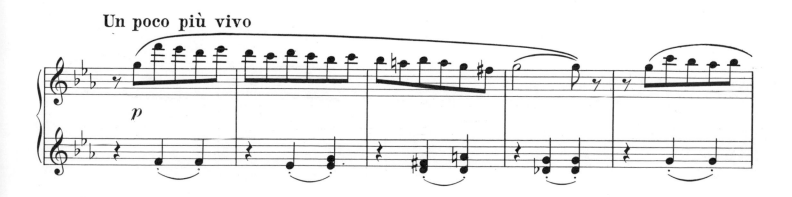

Secondo

Tempo I

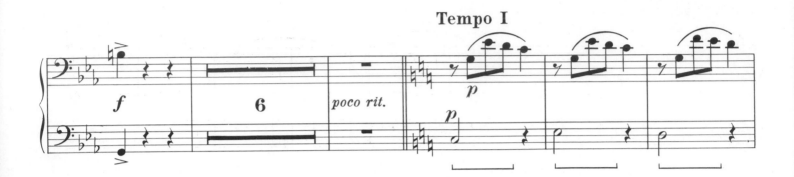

Tempo I

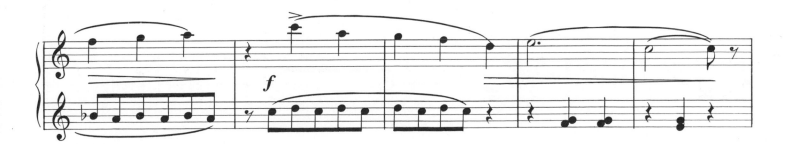

Un poco più vivo

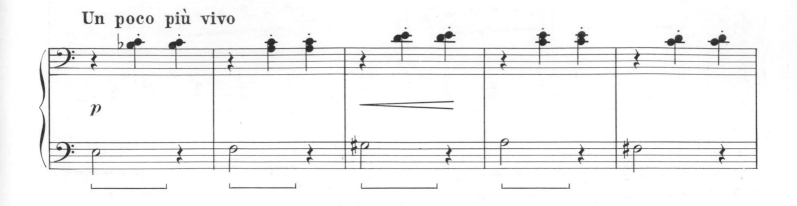

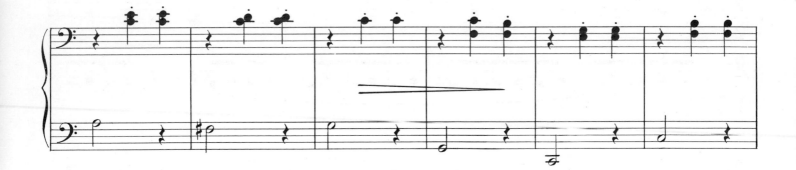

Un poco più vivo

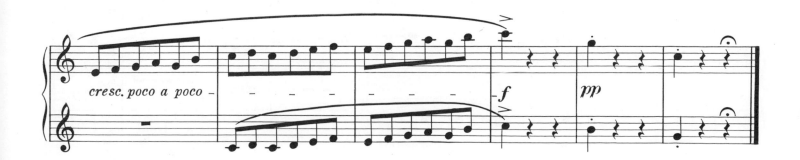

Sonata in D Major
Op. 6

Secondo

Ludwig van Beethoven
(1770-1827)

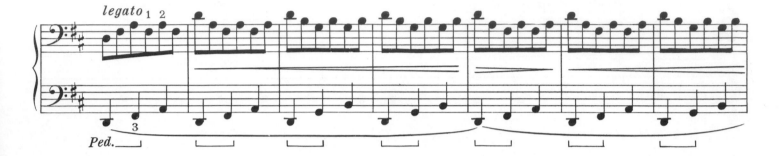

Sonata in D Major
Op. 6

Primo

Ludwig van Beethoven
(1770-1827)

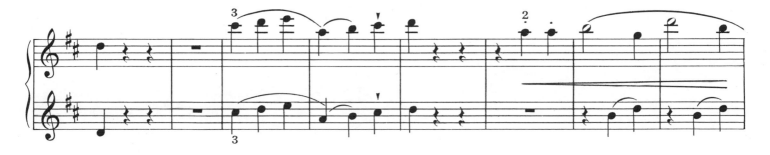

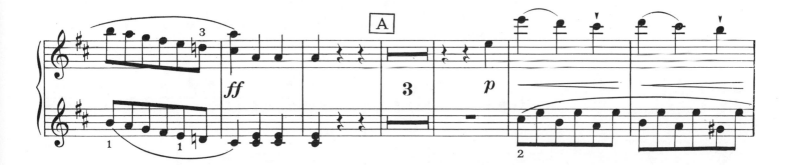

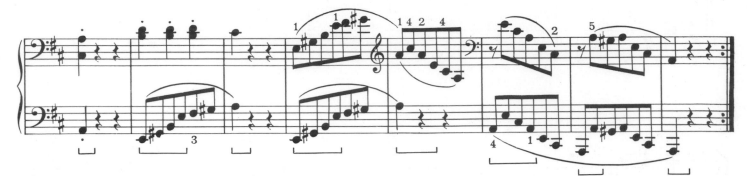

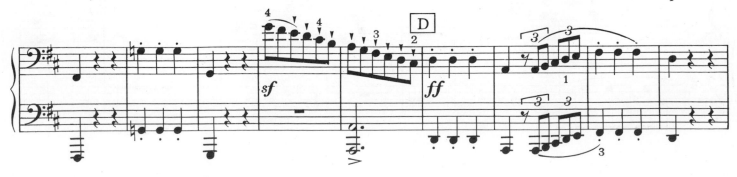

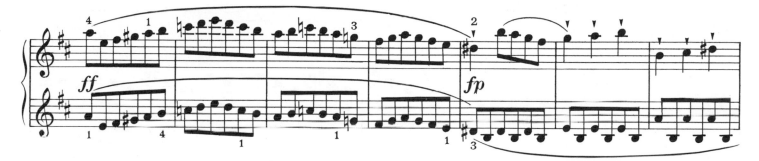

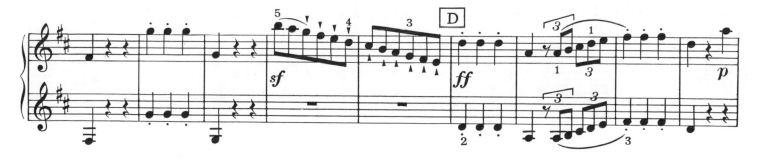

Primo

Primo

Primo

25

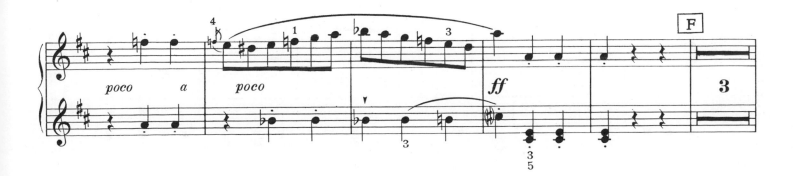

S. M. L. 6

Secondo

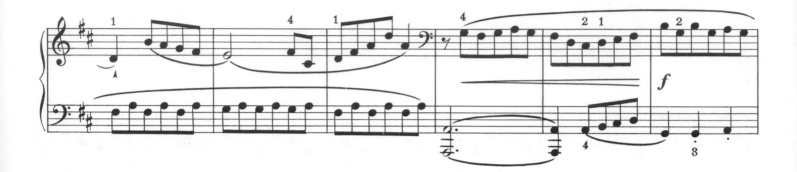

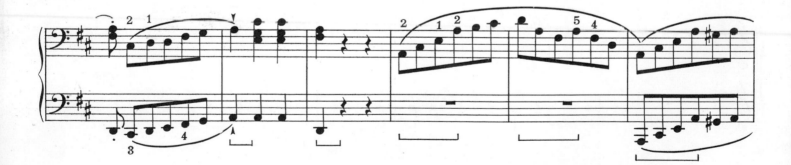

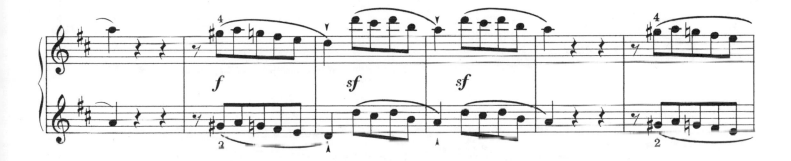

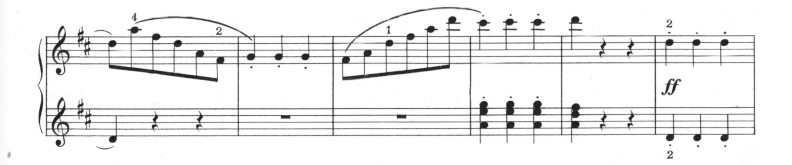

Secondo

Moderato

RONDO
Moderato

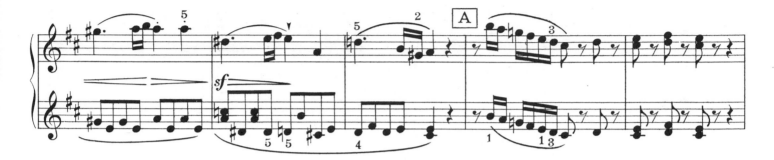

Secondo

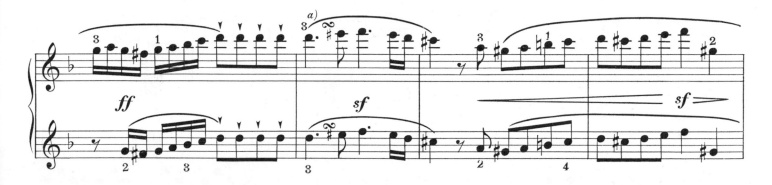

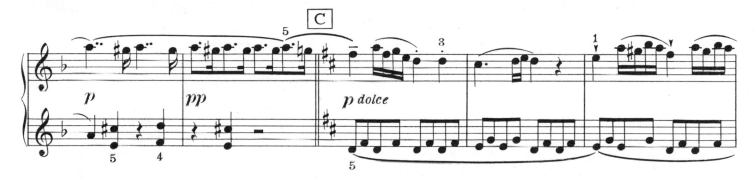

Secondo

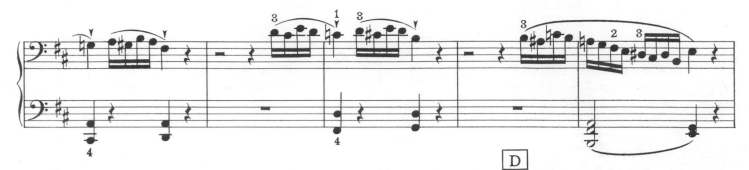

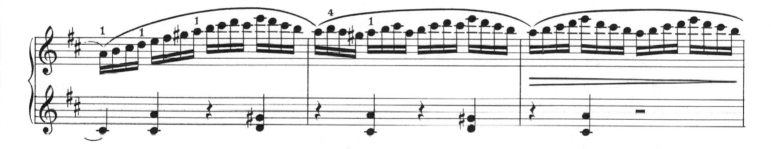

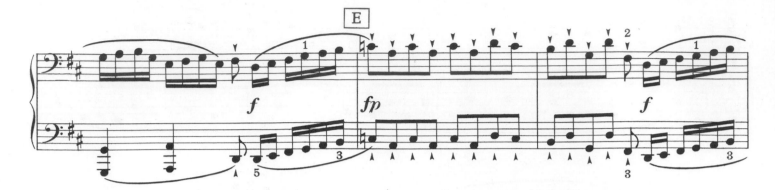

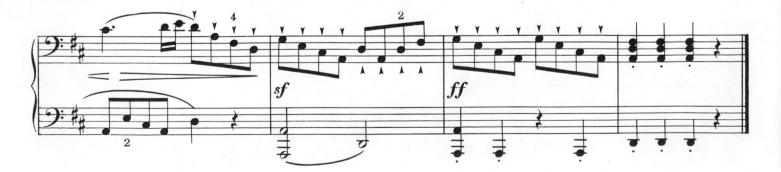

Primo

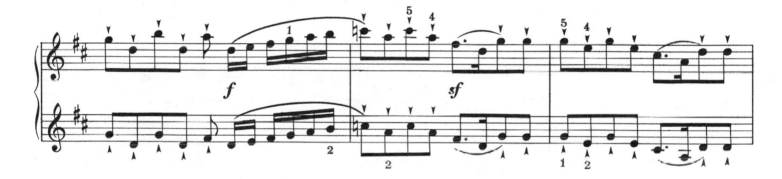

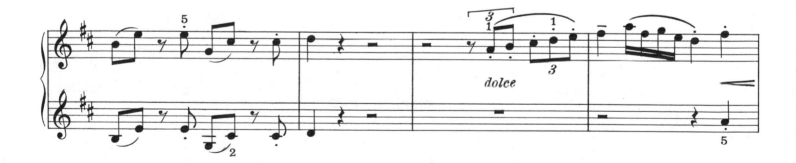

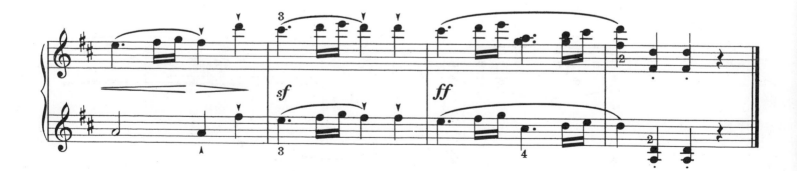

Sonatina in F Major

Secondo

Ludwig van Beethoven

Allegro assai

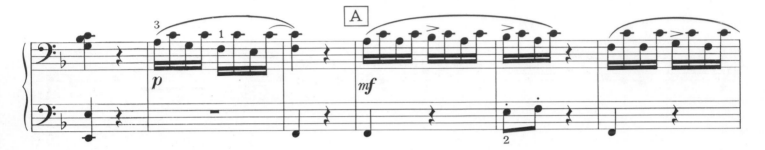

Sonatina in F Major

Primo

Ludwig van Beethoven

Allegro assai

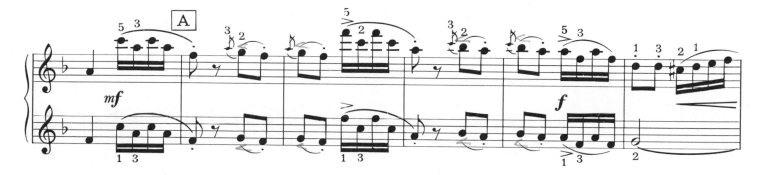

Primo

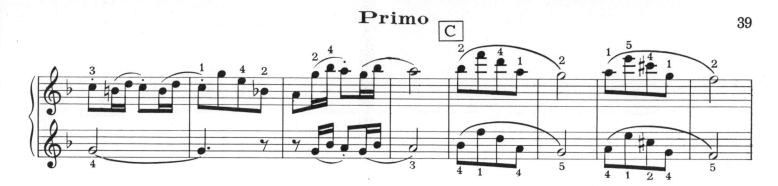

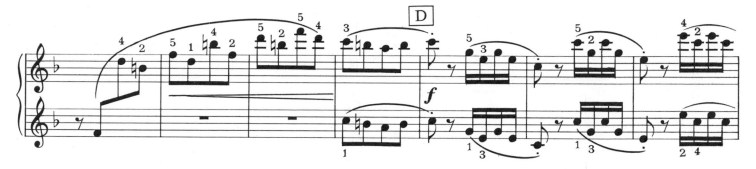

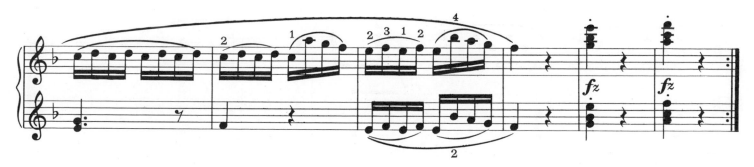

Rondo
Allegro

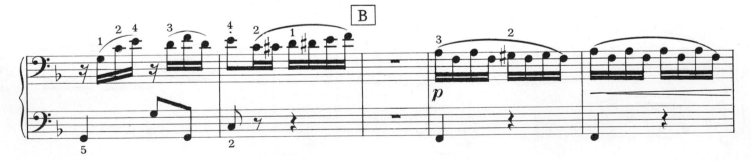

Primo

Rondo
Allegro

42

Secondo

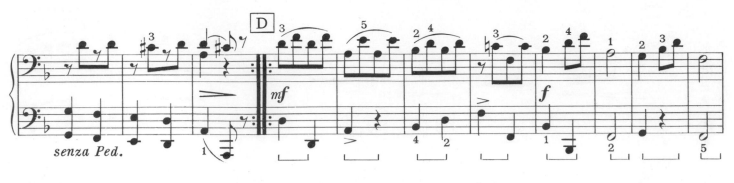

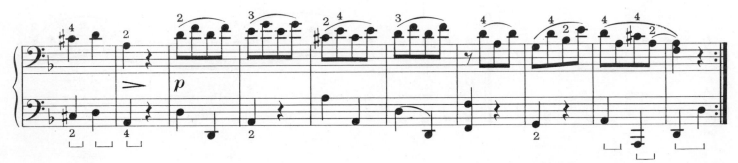

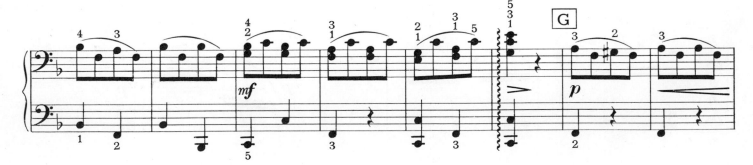

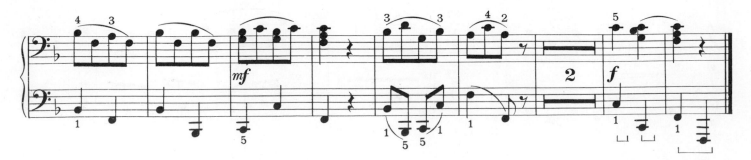

S. M. L. 6

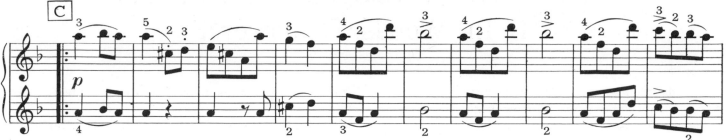

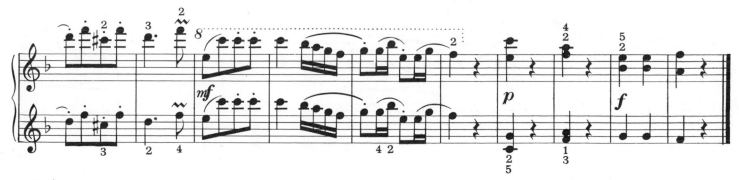

TWO LOVE SONG WALTZES
1. In Woods Embower'd
Op. 52a No. 9

In woods embower'd, 'neath azure sky,
A rosy maid looks from window high.
Well-guarded is she with lock and key:

With ten iron bars is her doorway made fast.
"Ha! ten iron bars are a jest to me;
As though they were glass, they shall shatter'd be."

Secondo

Johannes Brahms
(1833 - 1897)

TWO LOVE SONG WALTZES
1. In Woods Embower'd
Op. 52a No. 9

In woods embower'd, 'neath azure sky,
A rosy maid looks from window high.
Well guarded is she with lock and key:

With ten iron bars is her doorway made fast.
"Ha! ten iron bars are a jest to me;
As though they were glass, they shall shatter'd be,"

Primo

Johannes Brahms
(1833 - 1897)

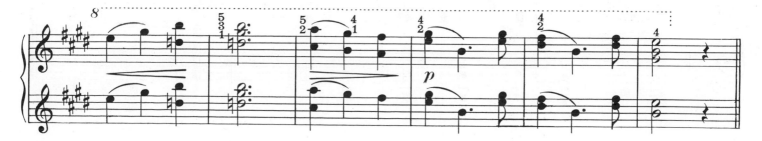

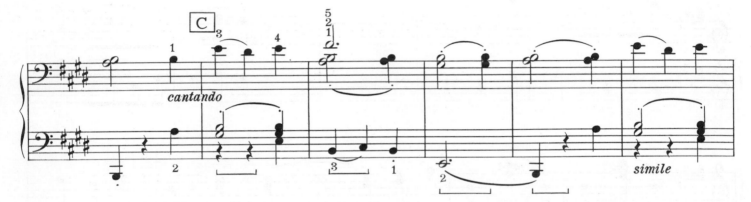

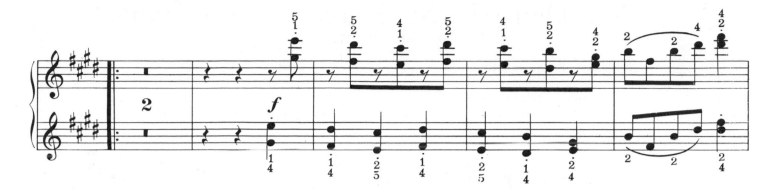

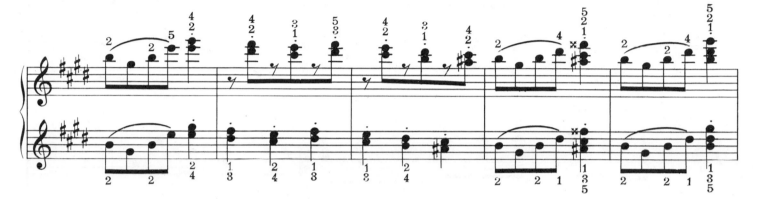

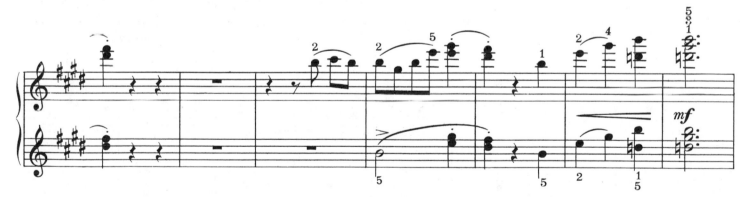

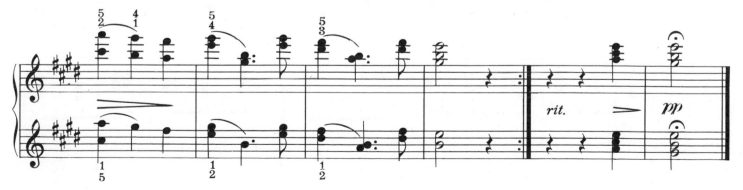

2. No, There Is No Bearing with Them

Op. 52a No. 11

No, there is no bearing with
these spiteful neighbors:
All they do is misconstrue
each other's labors.

Am I merry? then by
evil thoughts I'm haunted;
Am I sad? they say I
am with love demented.

Marcato

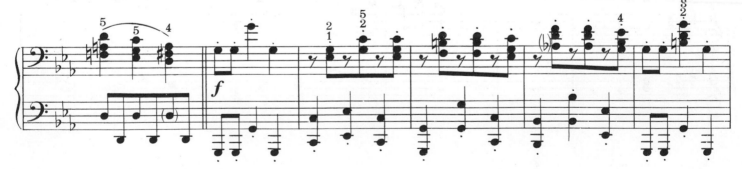

2. No, There Is No Bearing with Them

Op. 52a No. 11

No, there is no bearing with
these spiteful neighbors:
All they do is misconstrue
each other's labors.

Am I merry? then by
evil thoughts I'm haunted;
Am I sad? they say I
am with love demented.

Marcato

FIVE MELODIOUS PIECES

Secondo

1. Allegretto
Op. 149 No. 9

Anton Diabelli
(1781-1858)

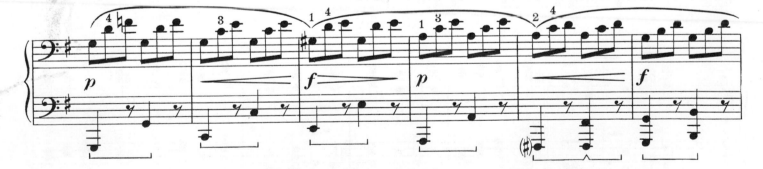

FIVE MELODIOUS PIECES

Primo

1. Allegretto
Op. 149 No. 9

Anton Diabelli
(1781 - 1858)

Secondo

2. Allegro
Op. 149 No. 10

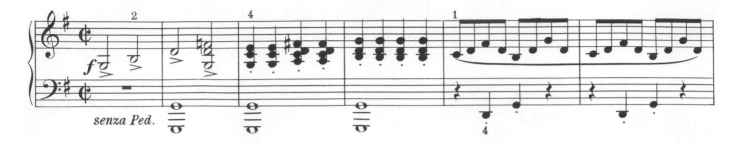

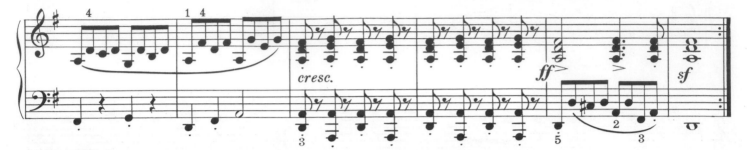

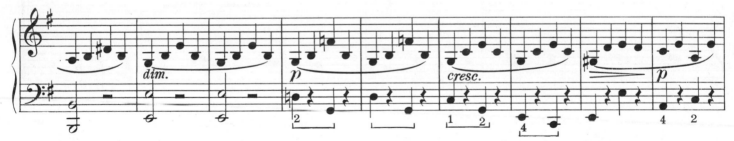

2. Allegro

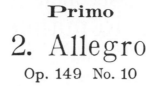

Op. 149 No. 10

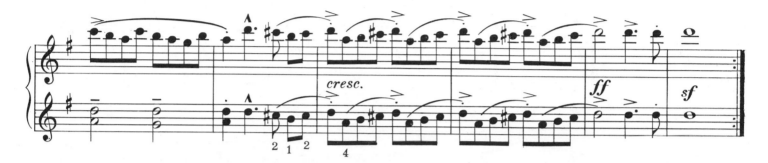

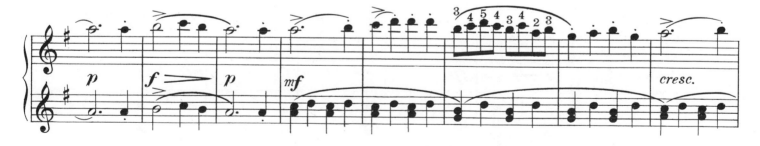

Secondo
3. Romance
Op. 149   No. 11

Andantino

4. Andante
Op. 149   No. 12

senza Ped.

3. Romance
Op. 149   No. 11

Andantino

4. Andante
Op. 149   No. 12

5. Allegro
Op. 149   No. 13

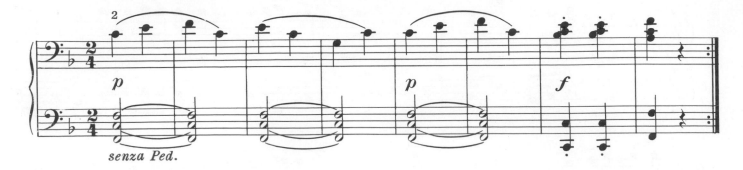

5. Allegro

Op. 149   No. 13

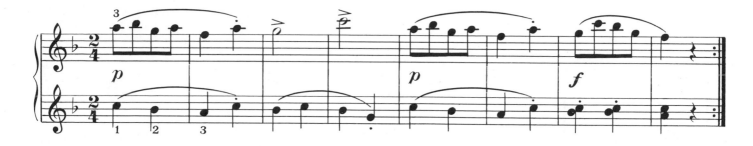

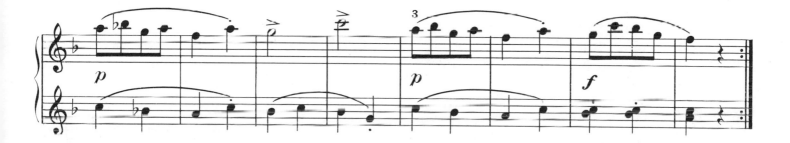

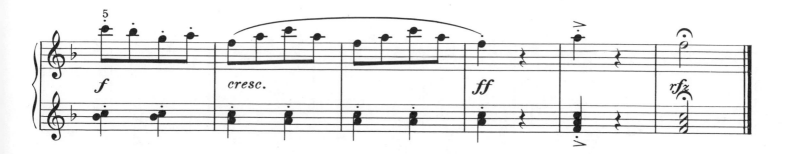

Waltz
Op. 3
Secondo

Ernst von Dohnányi
(1877 - 1960)

Allegro risoluto

Waltz
Op. 3

Primo

Ernst von Dohnányi
(1877 - 1960)

Allegro risoluto

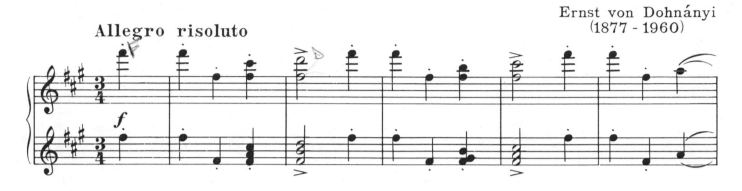

Primo

61

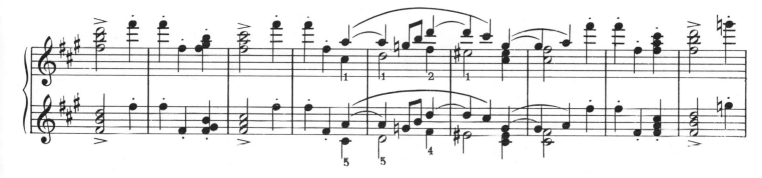

S. M. L. 6

Secondo

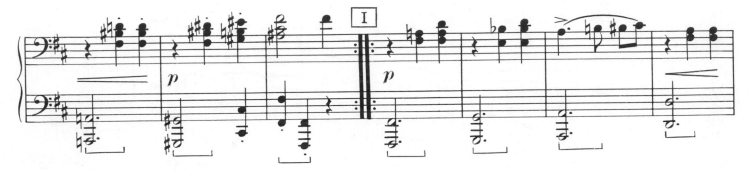

(sopra)
cross hands
with Secondo

S. M. L. 6

Secondo

L **Più allegro**

Secondo

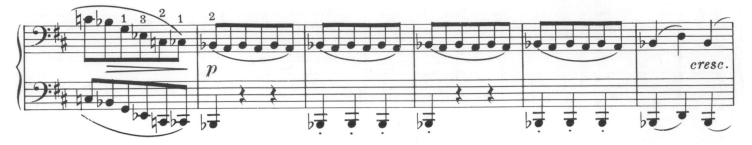

Secondo

(sopra)
cross hands
with Secondo

Kitty-Valse

Op. 56 No. 4

Secondo

Gabriel Fauré
(1845 - 1924)

Tempo di Valse

mf

Ped.   senza Ped.

f   *p*

senza Ped.

A

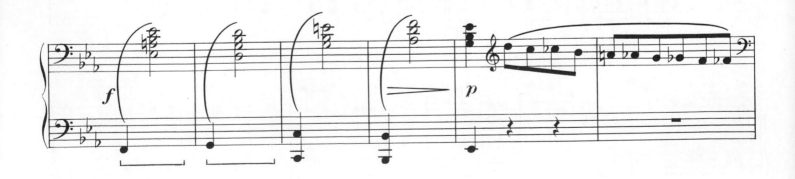

f   *p*

Kitty - Valse

Op. 56 No. 4

Primo

Gabriel Fauré
(1845-1924)

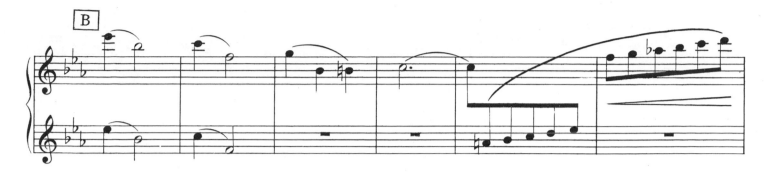

Secondo

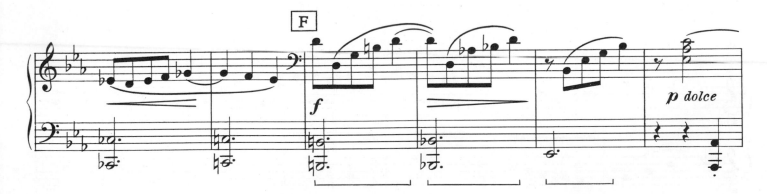

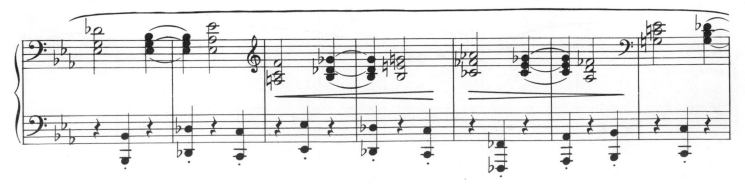

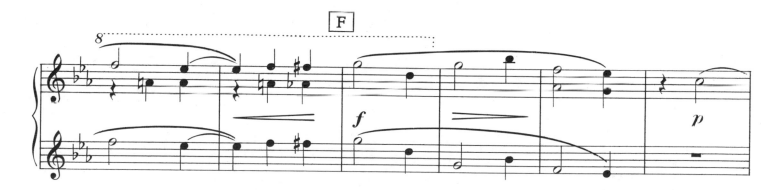

Secondo

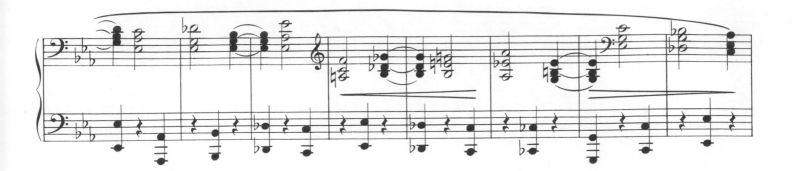

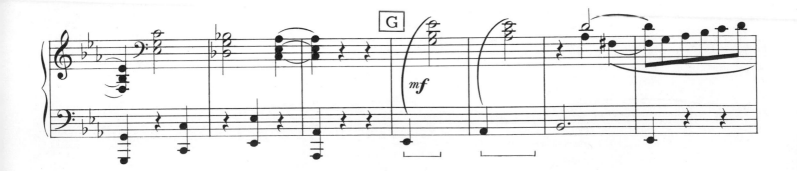

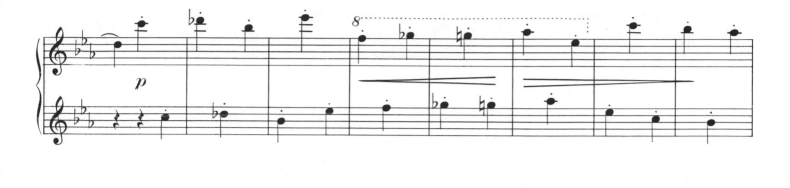

Secondo

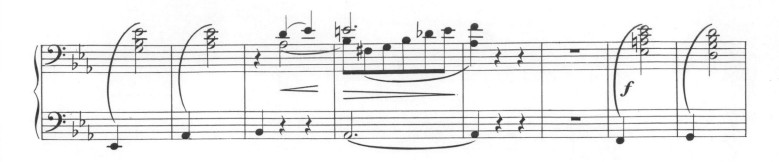

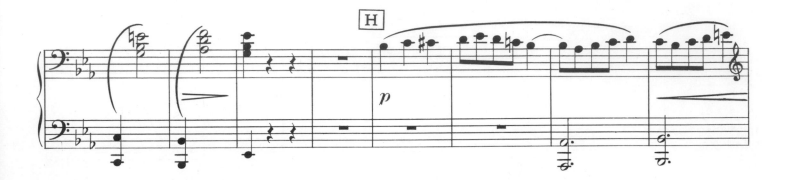

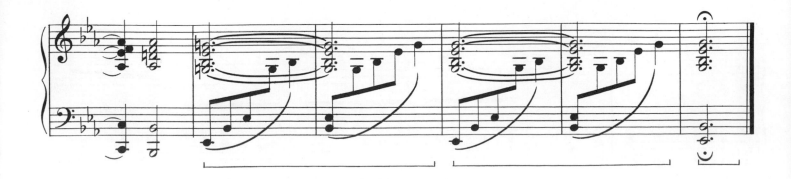

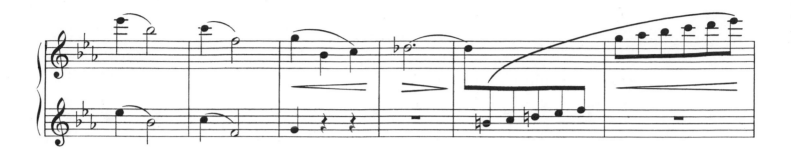

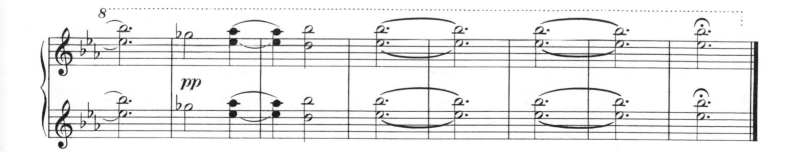

Norwegian Dance

Op. 35 No. 2

Secondo

Edvard Grieg
(1843-1907)

Allegretto tranquillo e grazioso (♩ = 76)

Norwegian Dance

Op. 35 No. 2

Primo

Edvard Grieg
(1843-1907)

Allegretto tranquillo e grazioso (♩ = 76)

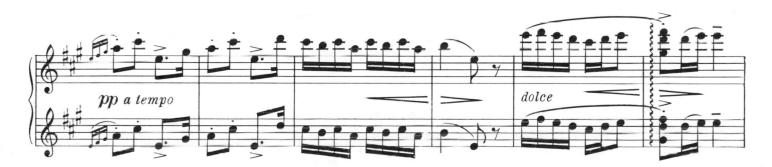

Allegro (♩ = 112)

senza Ped.

Tempo I

Tempo I

Forest Bird
Op. 43 No. 3

Secondo

Adolf Jensen
(1837-1879)

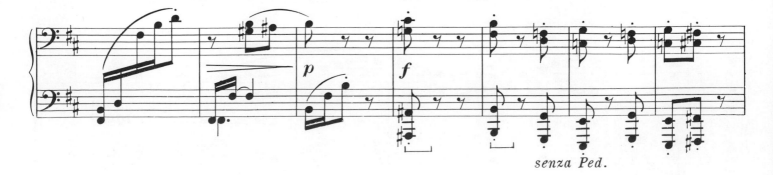

Forest Bird

Op. 43 No. 3

Primo

Allegretto

Adolf Jensen
(1837-1879)

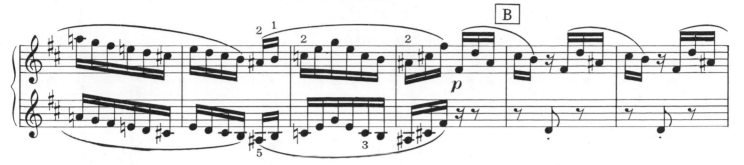

Dance Rhythms
Op. 14 No. 1

Secondo

Paul Juon
(1872–1940)

Alla marcia (♩ = 88)

Dance Rhythms

Op. 14 No. 1

Primo

Paul Juon
(1872-1940)

Dance Rhythms
Op. 14 No. 4

Secondo

Paul Juon

Dance Rhythms
Op. 14 No. 4

Primo

Paul Juon

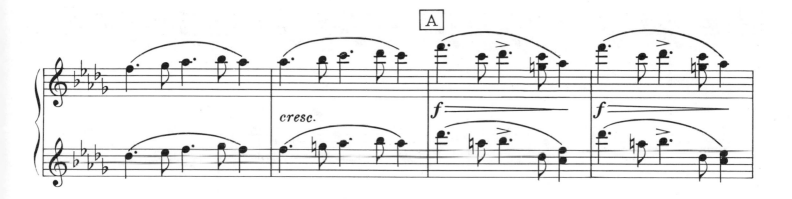

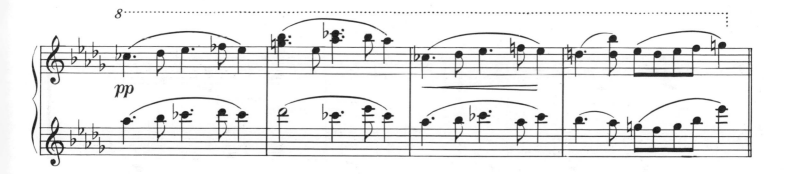

Secondo

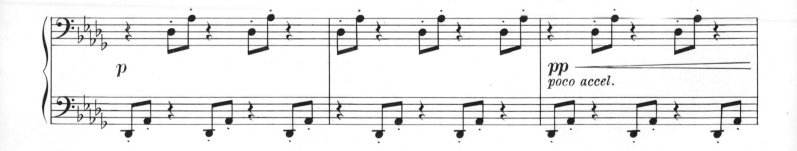

cresc. e rit.

pp a tempo

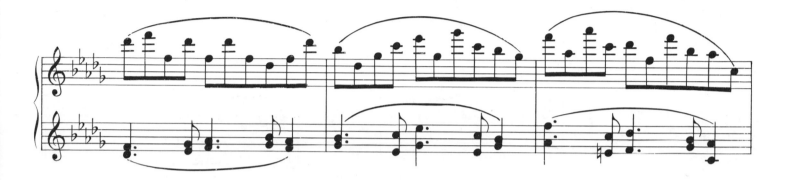

cresc.

dim.

p

pp

poco accel.

poco rit.

Theme and Variations
Op. 62 No. 10

Secondo

Richard Kleinmichel
(1846-1901)

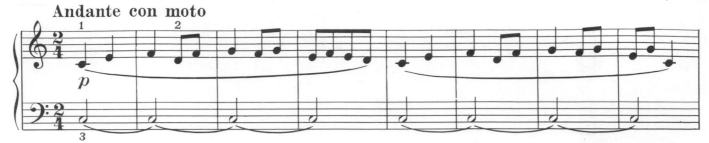

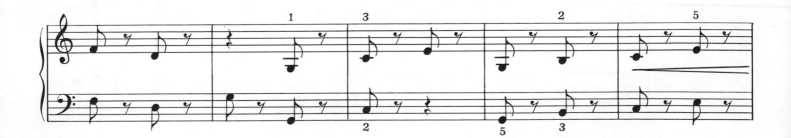

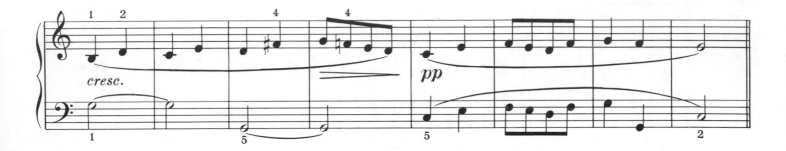

Theme and Variations
Op. 62 No. 10

Primo

Richard Kleinmichel
(1846-1901)

Andante con moto

Var. I

Secondo

Var. II

Var. III
Più lento

Var. II

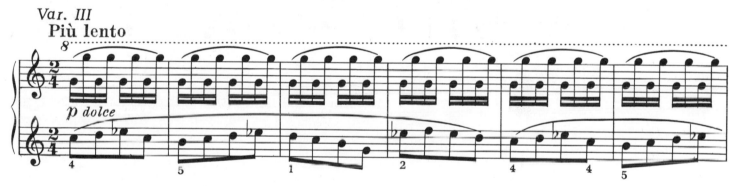

Var. III
Più lento

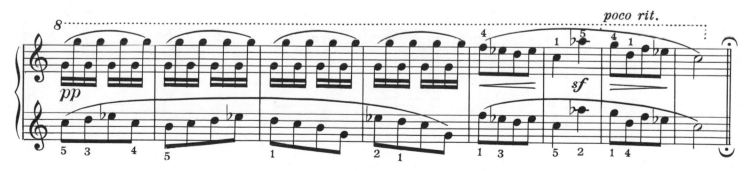

Secondo

Var. IV

Poco animato

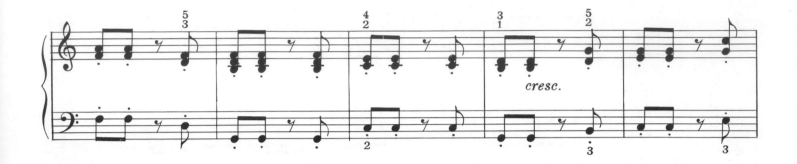

Poco animato

The Wanderer

Secondo

Louis Köhler
(1820-1886)

The Wanderer

Primo

Louis Köhler
(1820-1886)

Secondo

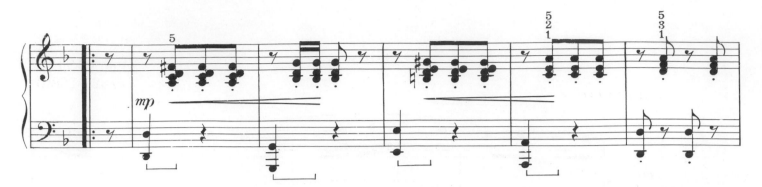

Primo

Minuet

from Op. 44, No. 3

Secondo

Friedrich Kuhlau
(1786-1832)

Allegro non tanto

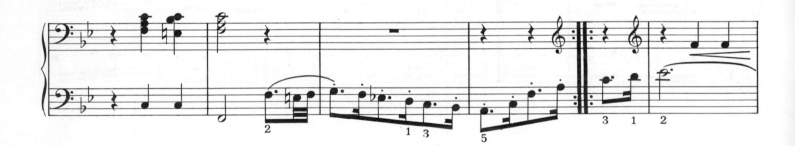

Minuet

from Op. 44, No. 3

Primo

Friedrich Kuhlau
(1786-1832)

S. M. L. 6

Secondo

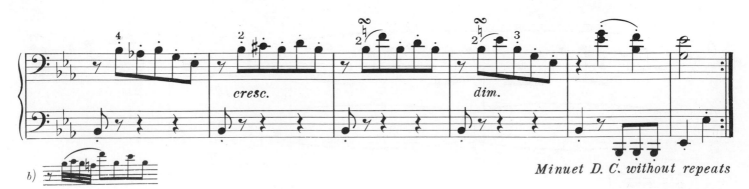

Minuet D. C. without repeats

Minuet D. C. without repeats

Allegro Brillant
Op. 92

Felix Mendelssohn
(1809 - 1847)

Secondo

Allegro assai vivace

Allegro Brillant

Op. 92

Primo

Felix Mendelssohn
(1809 - 1847)

Secondo

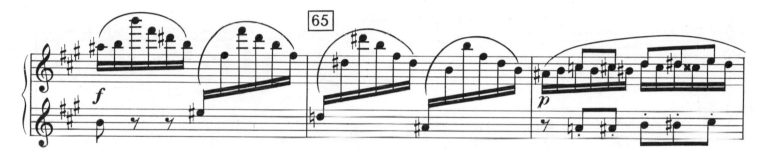

Secondo

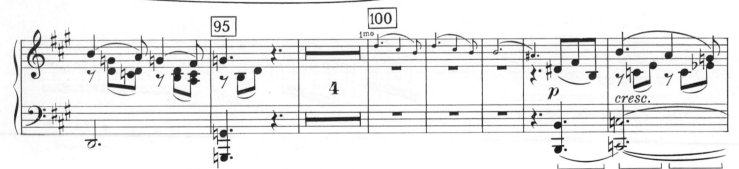

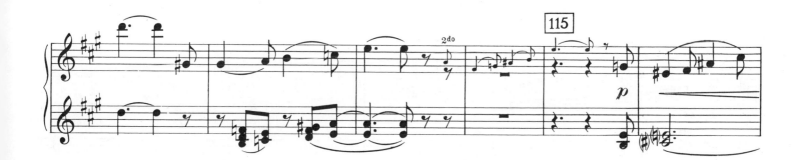

Secondo

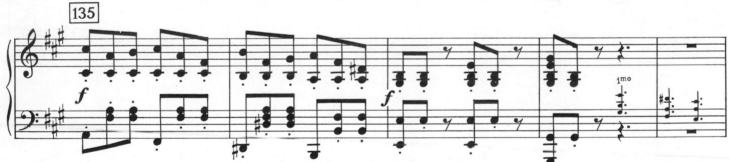

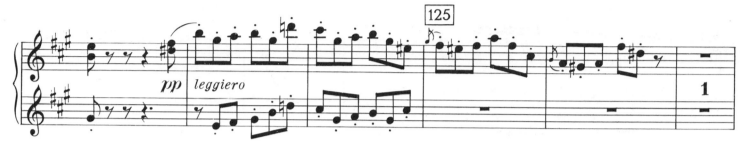

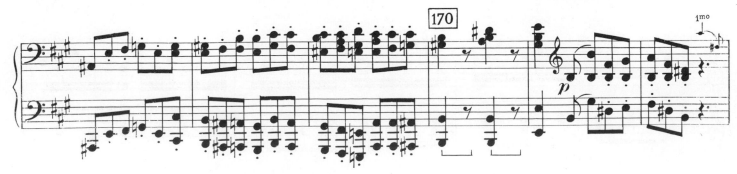

Primo

Secondo

sempre pp

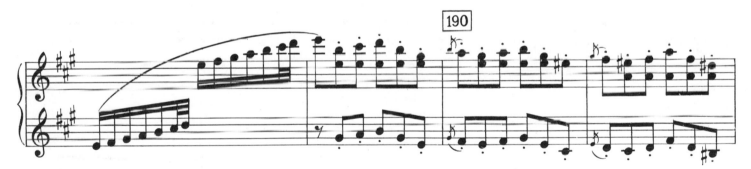

Secondo

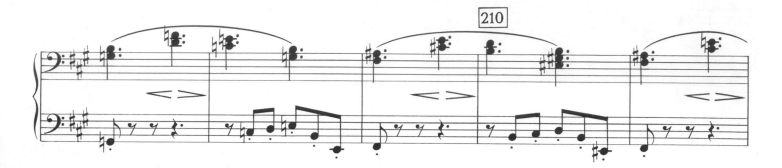

Secondo

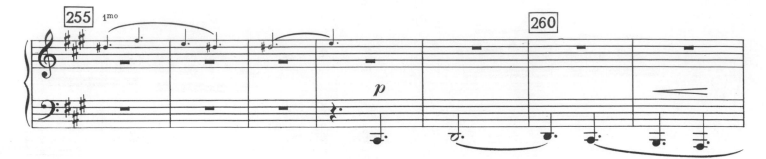

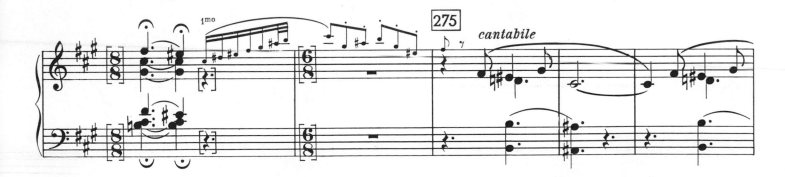

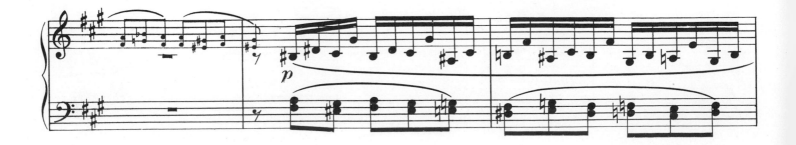

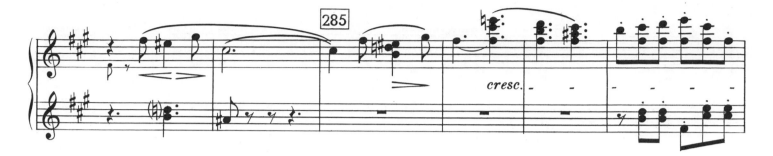

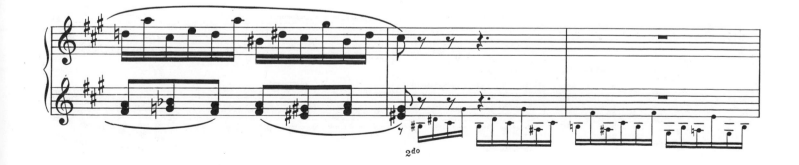

Secondo

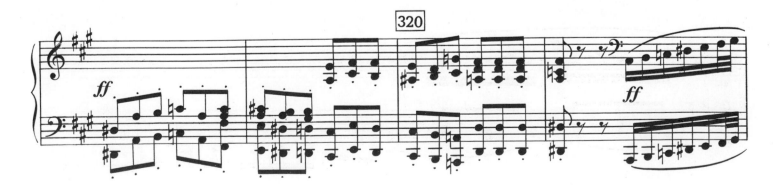

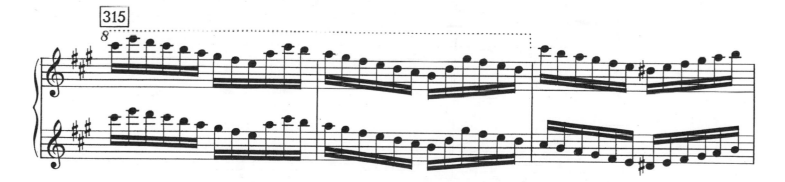

Secondo

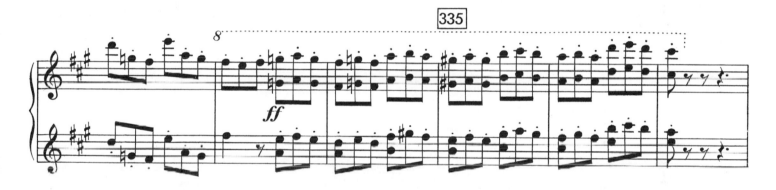

Secondo

138

Secondo

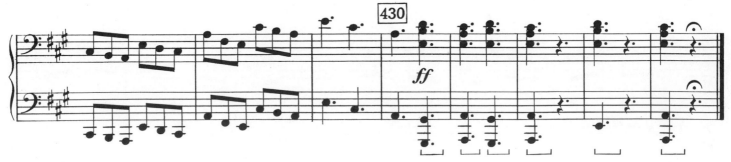

S. M. L. 6

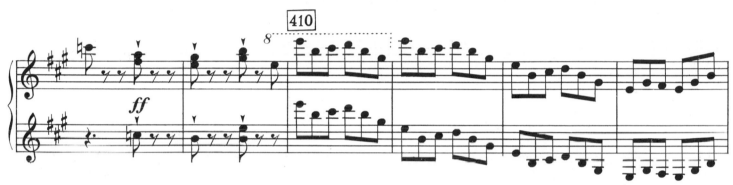

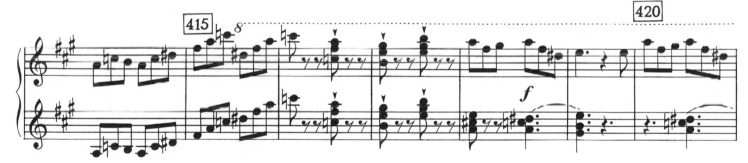

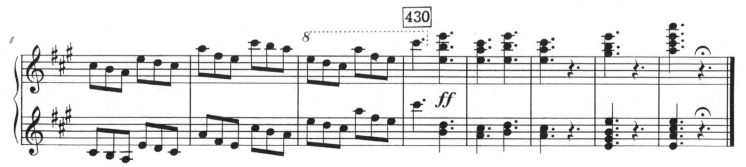

Bolero
Op. 12 No. 5
Secondo

Moritz Moszkowski
(1854-1925)

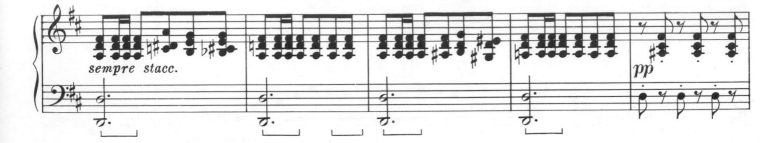

Bolero

Op. 12 No. 5

Primo

Moritz Moszkowski
(1854-1925)

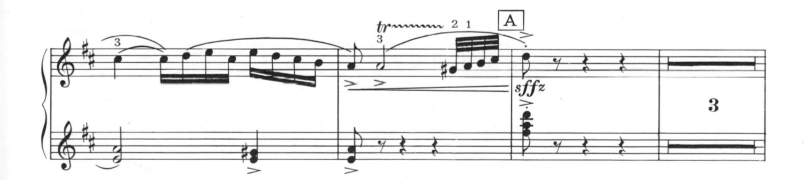

Secondo

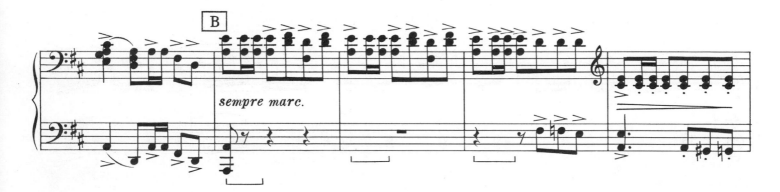

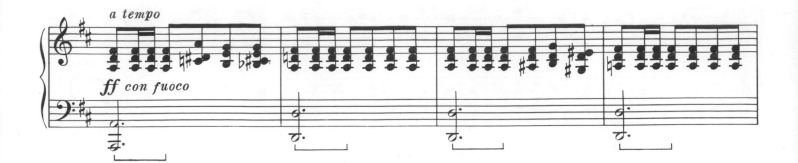

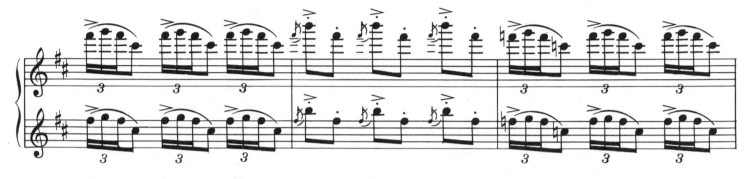

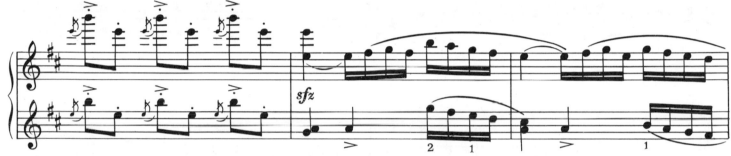

Secondo

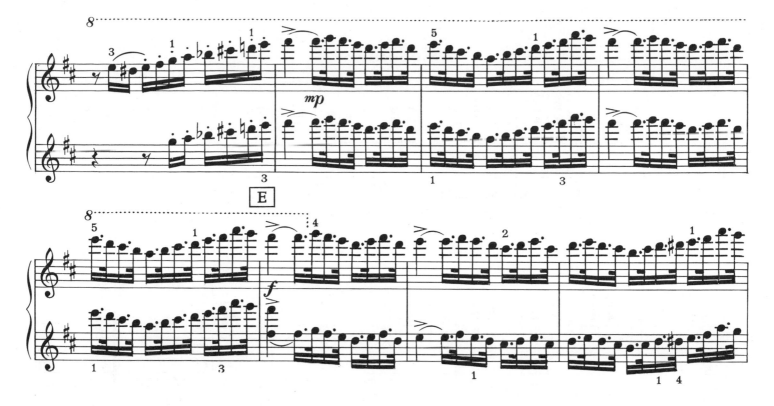

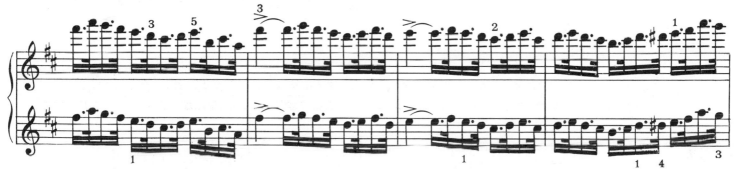

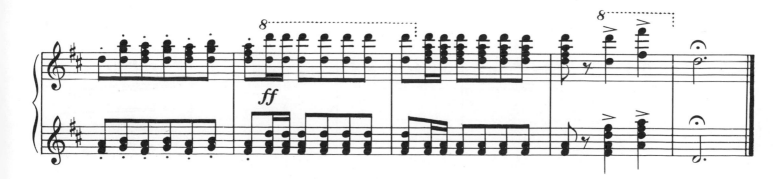

Spanish Dance
Op. 12 No. 1

Secondo

Allegro brioso

Moritz Moszkowski

Spanish Dance

Op. 12 No. 1

Primo

Moritz Moszkowski

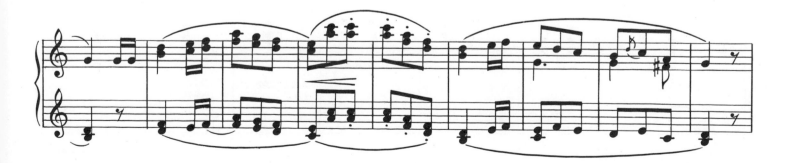

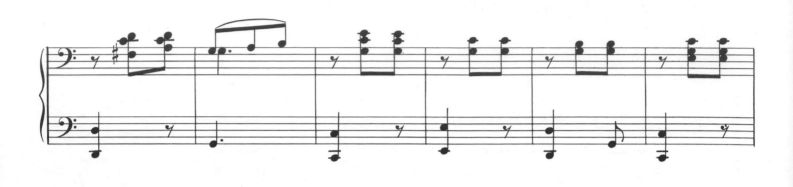

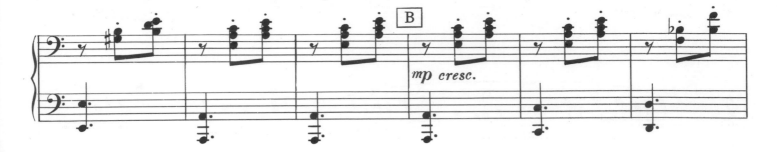

Sonata in B-flat Major

K. 358

Secondo

Wolfgang Amadeus Mozart
(1756-1791)

Sonata in B-flat Major

K. 358

Primo

Wolfgang Amadeus Mozart
(1756-1791)

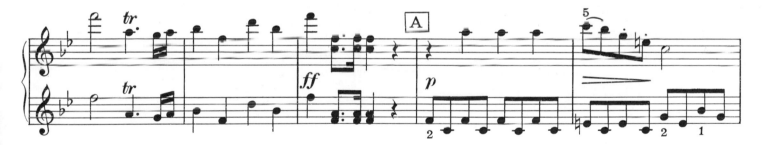

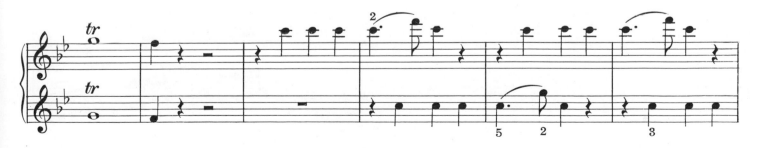

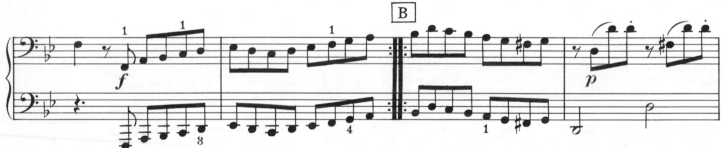

Secondo

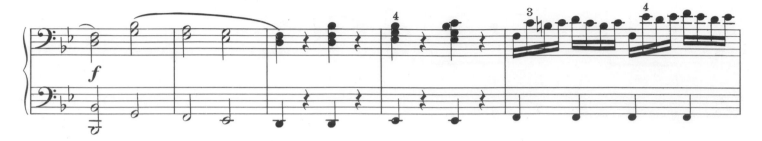

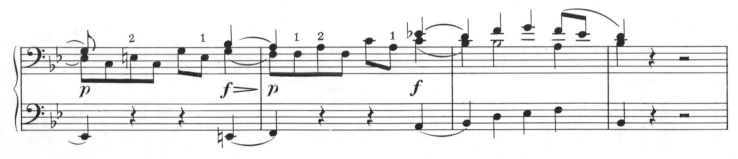

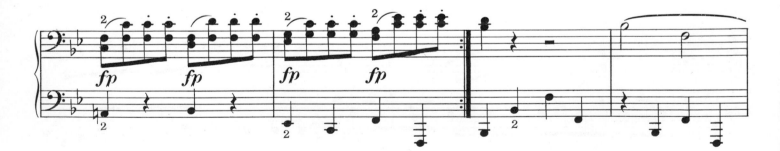

Primo

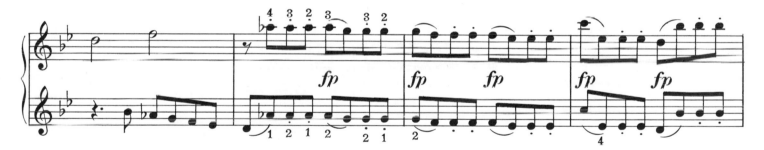

Adagio

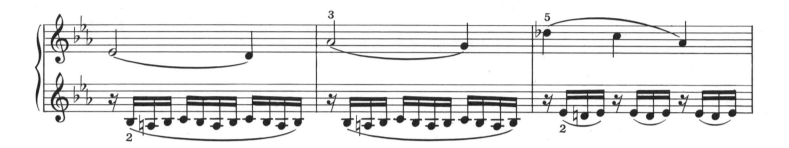

Secondo

Primo

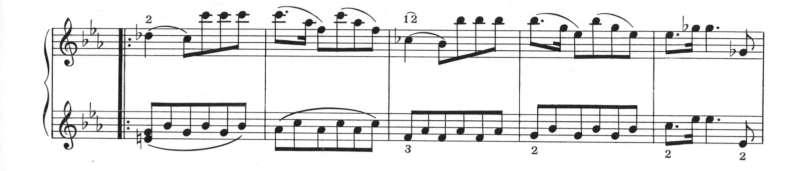

Secondo

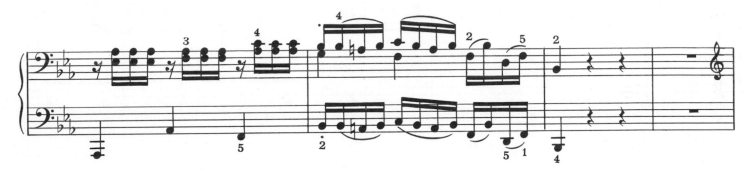

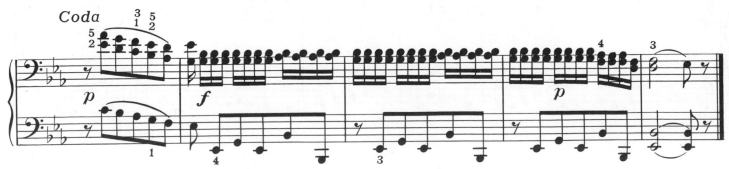

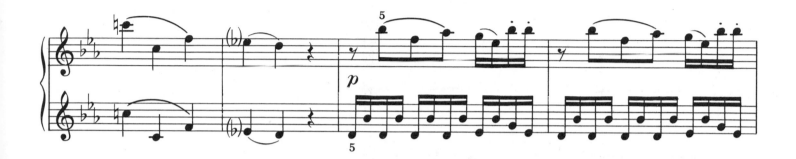

Molto presto

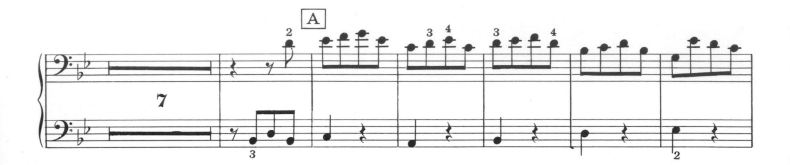

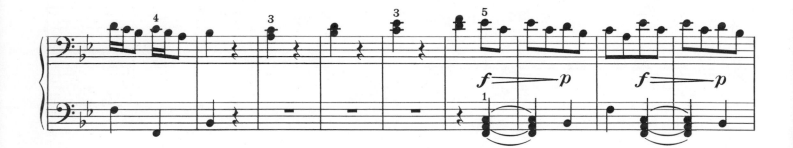

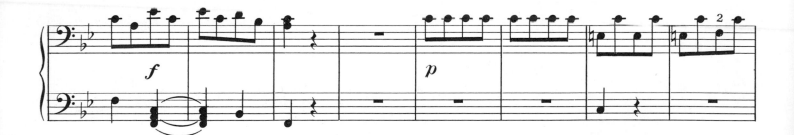

Primo

Molto presto

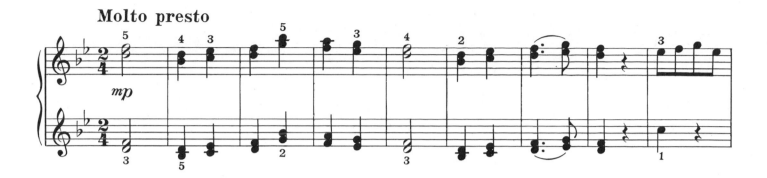

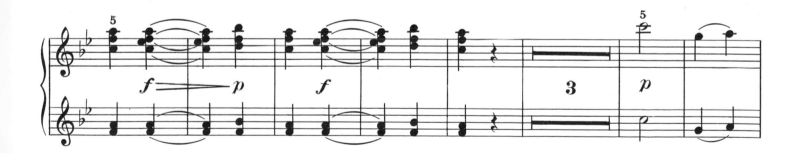

Secondo

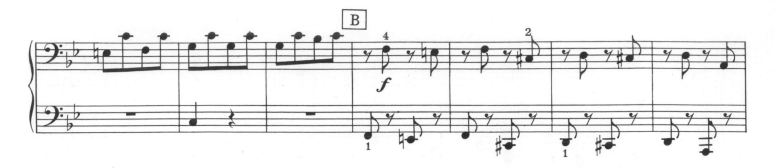

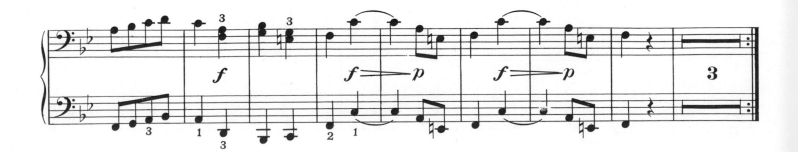

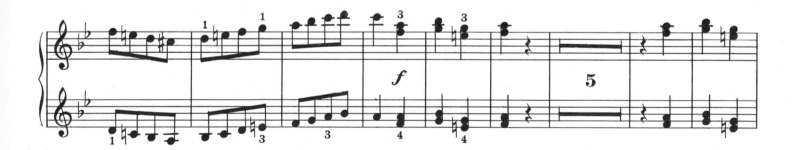

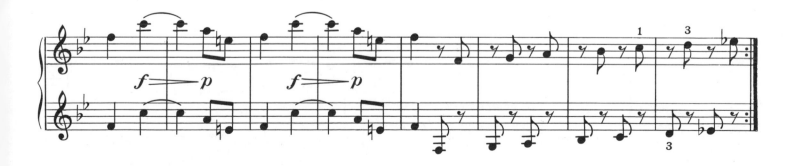

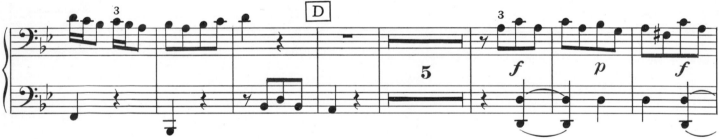

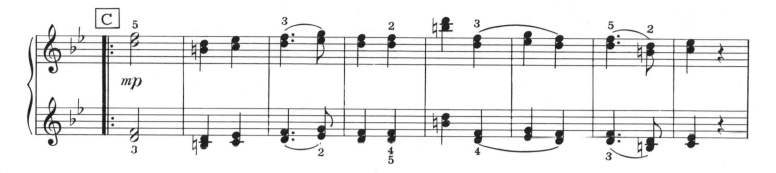

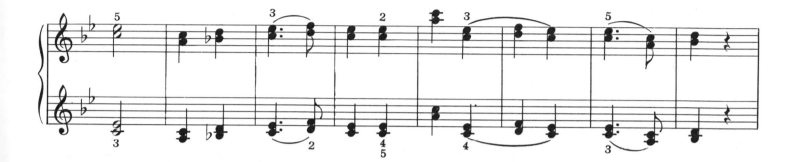

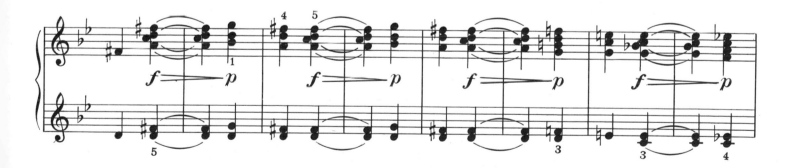

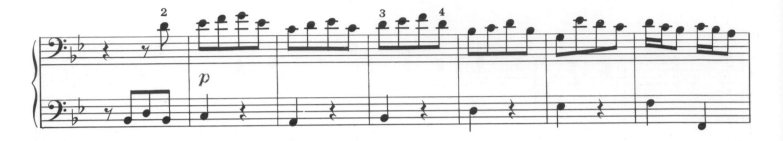

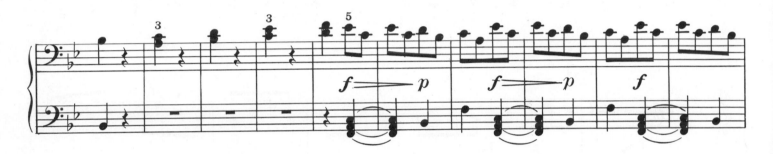

Secondo

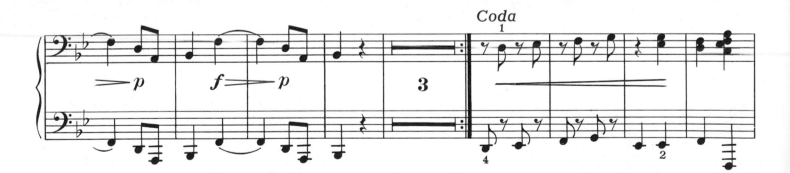

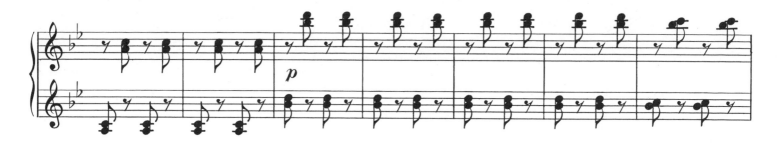

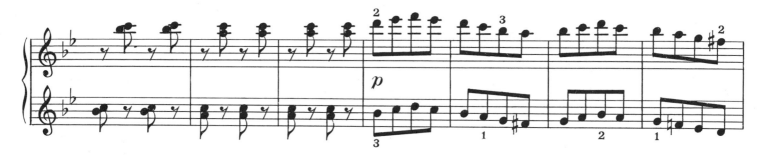

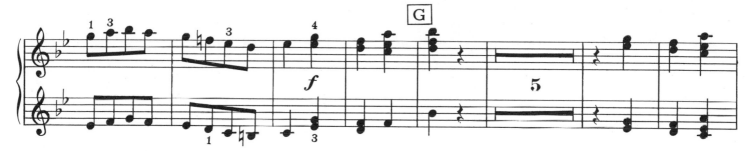

Coda

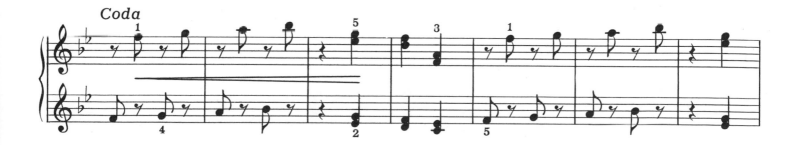

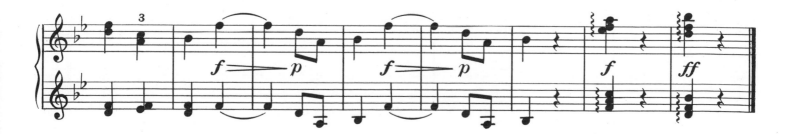

Polish Dance

from the *Tatra Album*

Op. 12 No. 1

Secondo

Ignace Paderewski
(1860 - 1941)

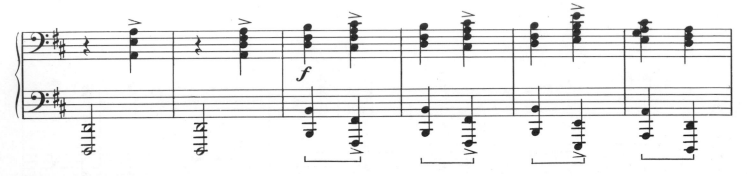

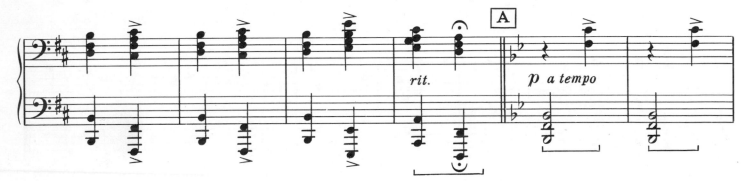

Polish Dance

from the *Tatra Album*

Op. 12 No. 1

Allegro con brio

Primo

Ignace Paderewski
(1860-1941)

Secondo

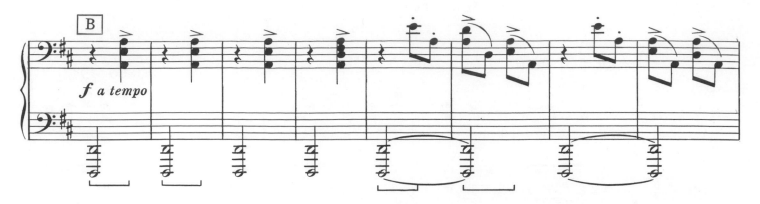

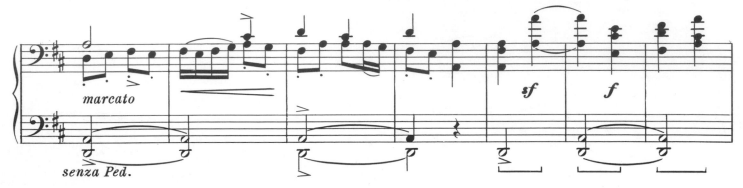

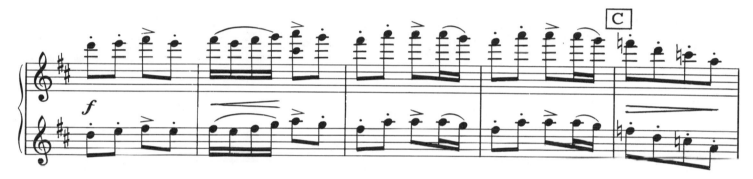

Secondo

E **Poco moderato**

Primo

E Poco moderato

Secondo

Secondo

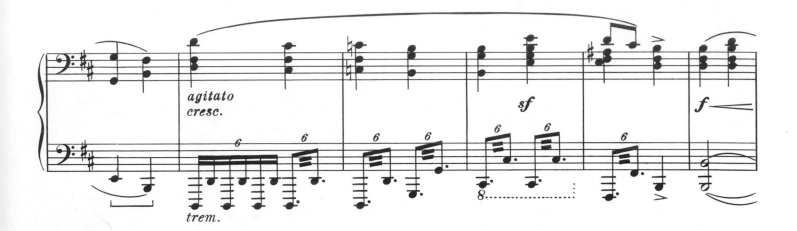

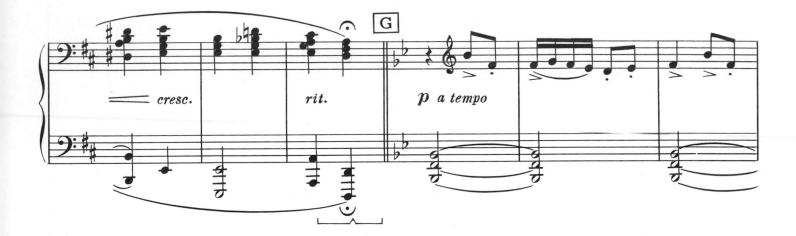

H Poco più mosso

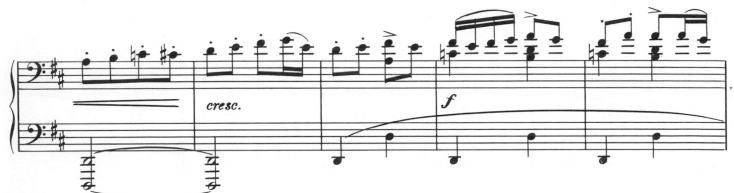

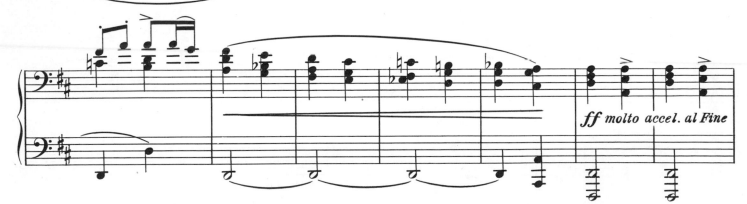

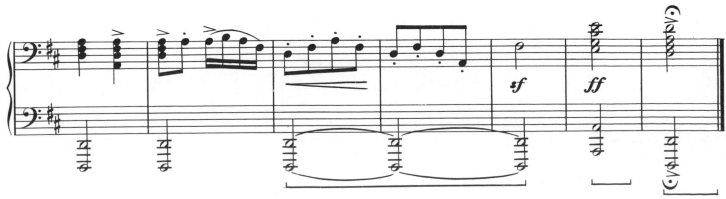

H **Poco più mosso**

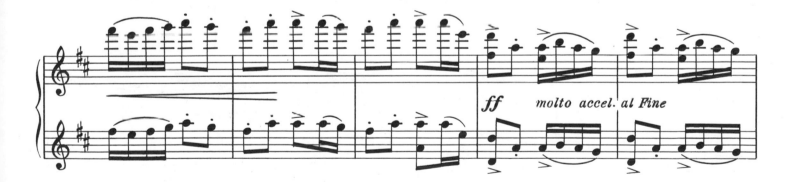

Barcarolle

Secondo

Eduard Poldini
(1869-1957)

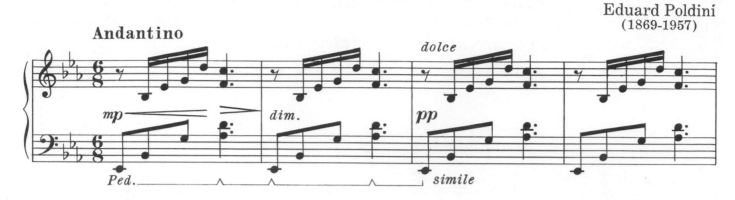

Barcarolle

Primo

Eduard Poldini
(1869-1957)

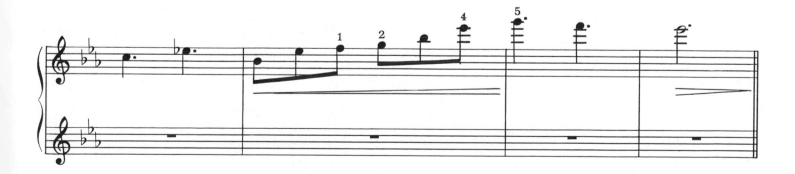

Secondo

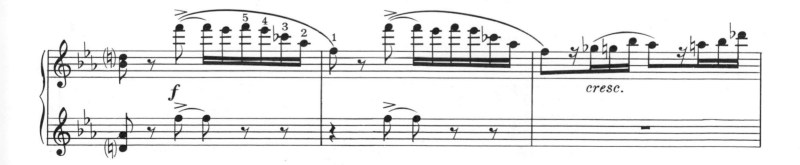

Secondo

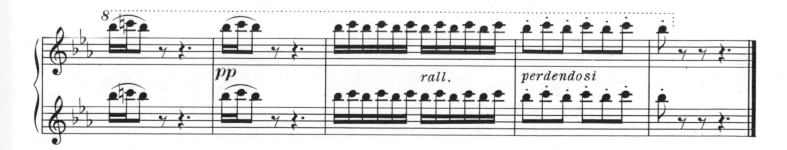

Gavotte
Secondo

Eduard Poldini

Gavotte
Primo

Eduard Poldini

Allegro moderato

Più mosso

Tempo I

S. M. L. 6

TWO DANCES
from *Petite Suite*
1. Tarantella
Op. 30 No. 3

Secondo

Vladimir Rebikov
(1866 - 1920)

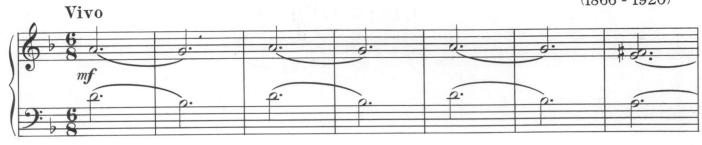

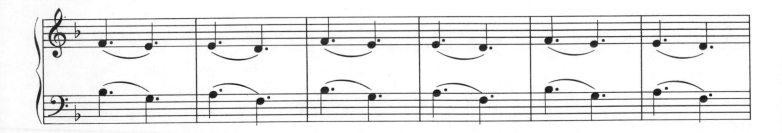

TWO DANCES
from *Petite Suite*
1. Tarantella
Op. 30 No. 3

Primo

Vladimir Rebikov
(1866 - 1920)

* keep hand low; *Secondo* will play a B - flat above the *Primo* part in the next measure.

S.M.L. 6

Secondo

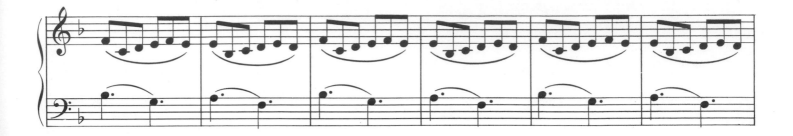

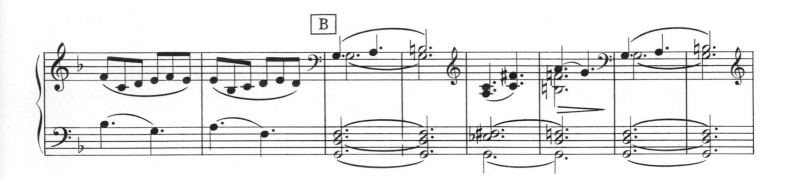

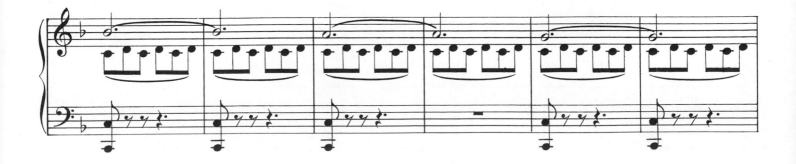

Secondo

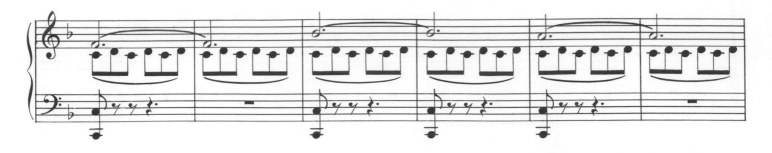

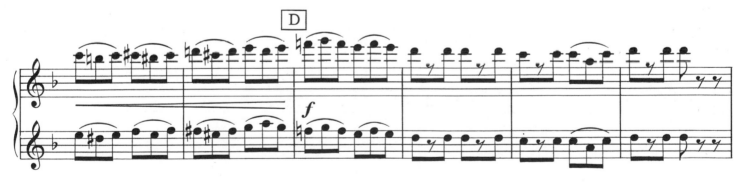

Secondo

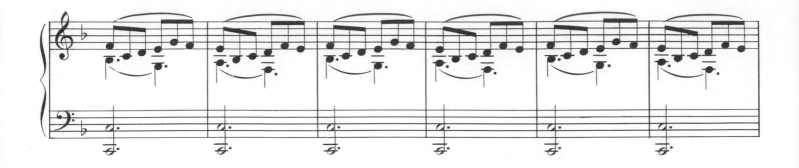

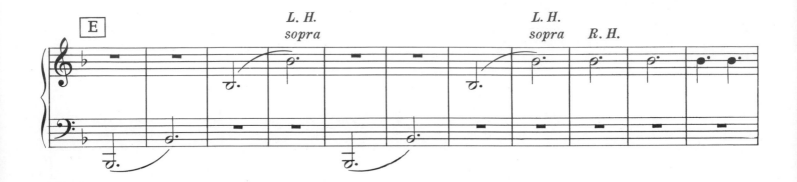

E

infra   *infra*

dim.   *pp*

2. Waltz

Op. 30 No. 1

Secondo

2. Waltz

Op. 30 No. 1

Primo

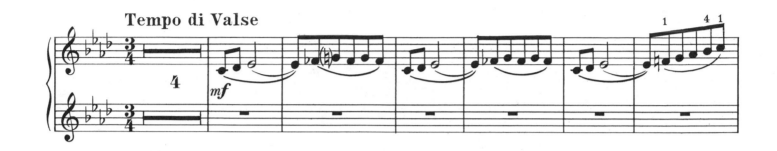

Secondo

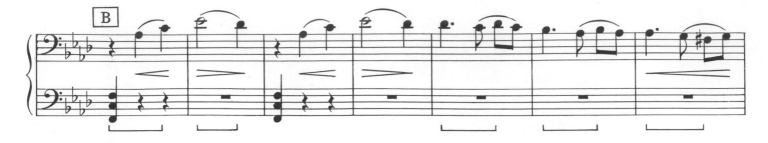

Secondo

E Più mosso

F

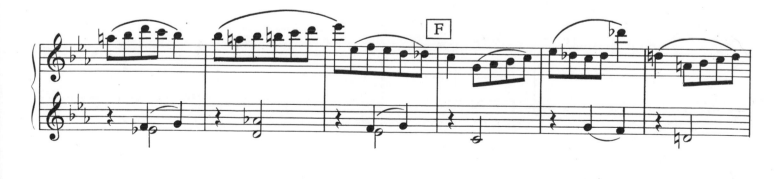

Secondo

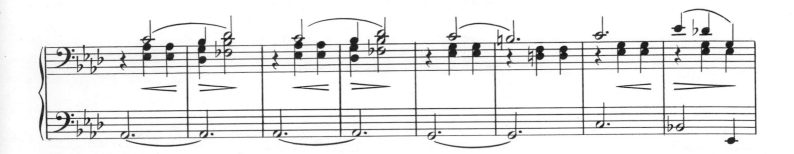

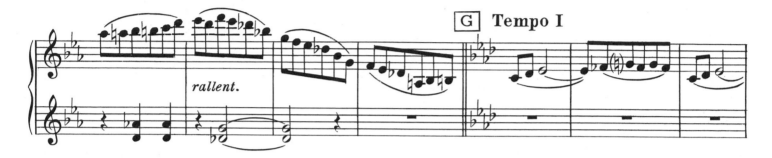

Secondo

Love's Happiness

Op. 165 No. 7

Secondo

Carl Reinecke
(1824 - 1910)

Love's Happiness

Op. 165 No. 7

Primo

Carl Reinecke
(1824 - 1910)

Secondo

Tempo I

Primo

Tempo I

Rustic Dance

Op. 122b No. 6

Secondo

Carl Reinecke

Tempo di Valzer, lento

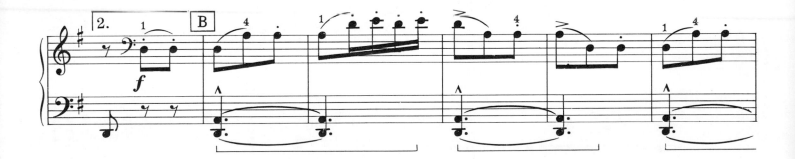

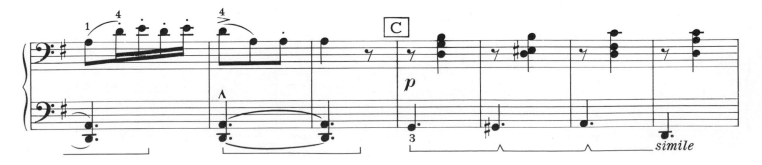

Rustic Dance

Op. 122b No. 6

Primo

Tempo di Valzer, lento

Carl Reinecke

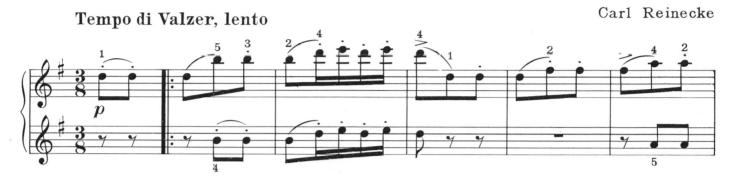

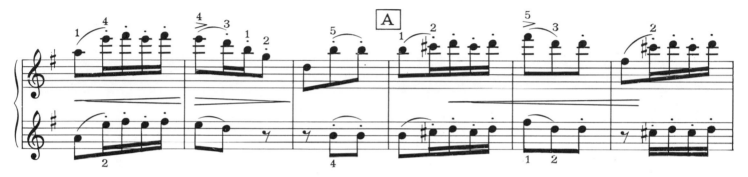

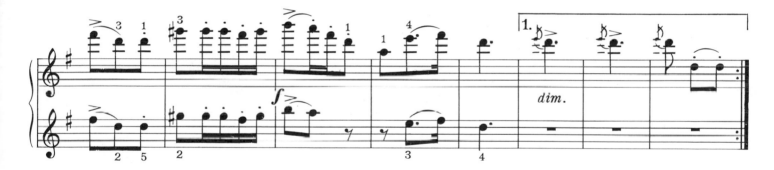

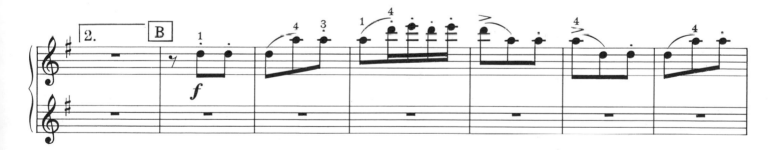

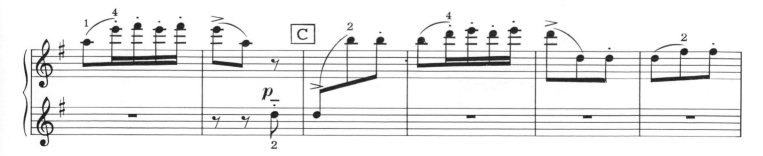

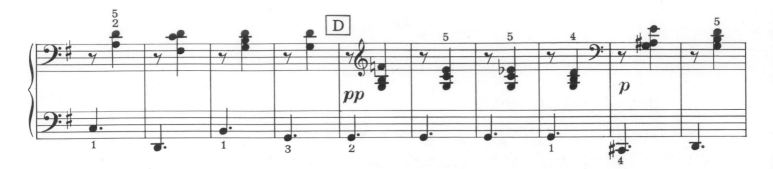

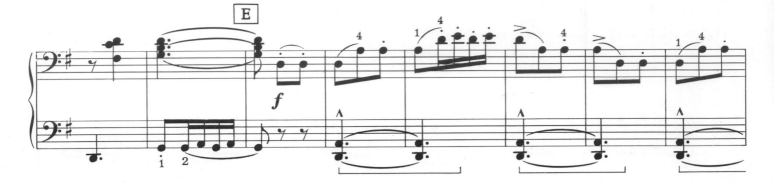

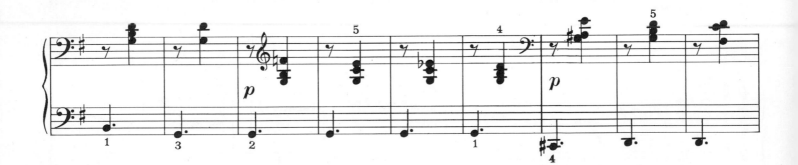

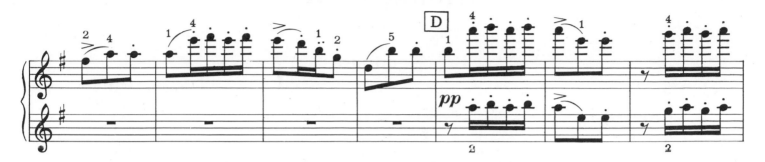

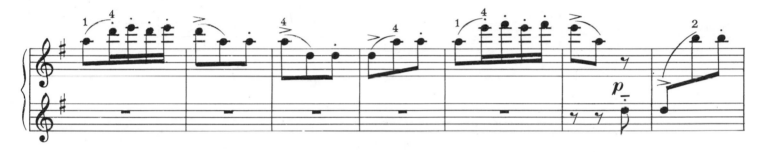

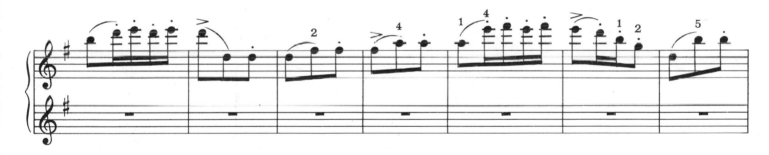

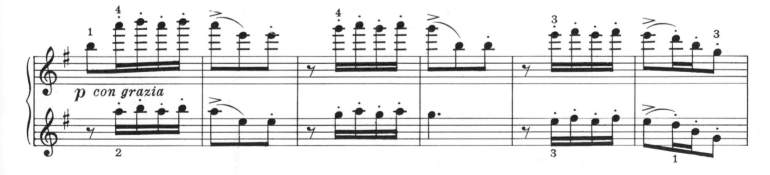

S.M.L.6

Album Leaf
Op. 81

Secondo

Camille Saint-Saëns
(1835-1921)

Andantino quasi allegretto

Album Leaf
Op. 81

Primo

Camille Saint-Saëns
(1835-1921)

Andantino quasi allegretto

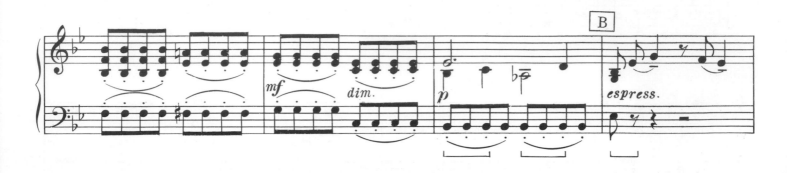

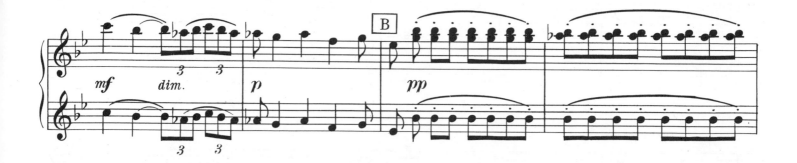

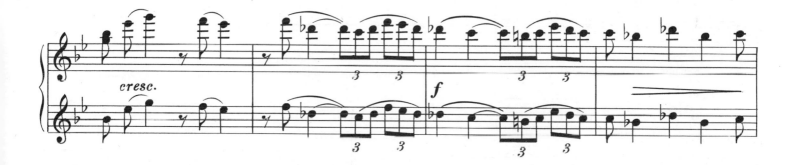

Secondo

Polonaise
Op. 61 No. 1

Secondo

Franz Schubert
(1797-1828)

Polonaise

Op. 61 No. 1

Primo

Franz Schubert
(1797-1828)

Fine

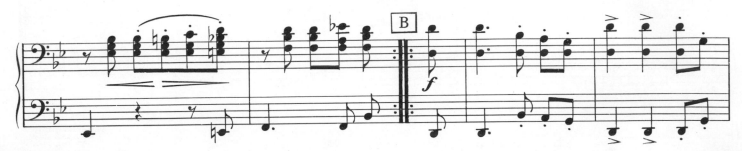

Polonaise da Capo

Polonaise da Capo

Three Souvenir Waltzes
Op. 64

1

Secondo

Eduard Schütt
(1856 - 1933)

Three Souvenir Waltzes

Op. 64

1

Primo

Eduard Schütt
(1856 - 1933)

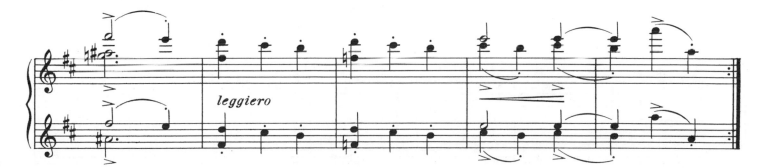

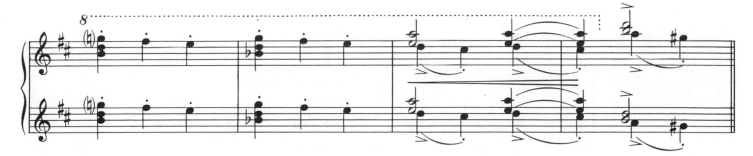

Secondo

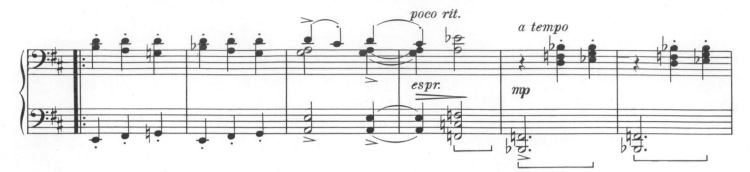

Secondo

Moderato un poco moto

Poco animato

Tempo I

2

Moderato un poco moto
con grazia

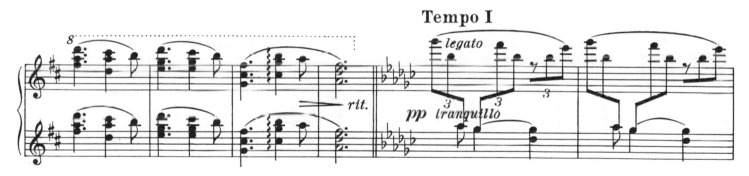

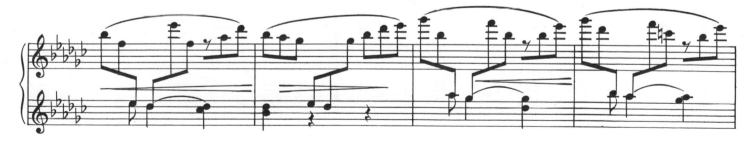

Secondo

3

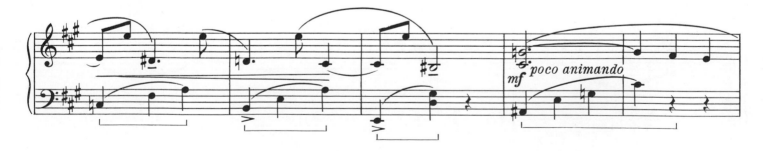

3

Allegro grazioso

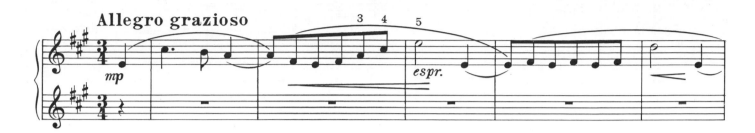

Più animato

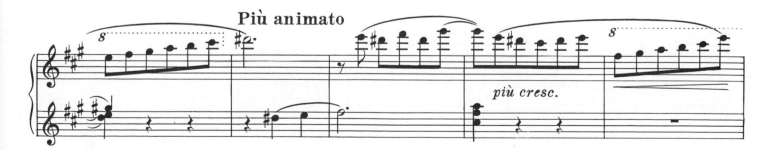

Secondo

Tempo I

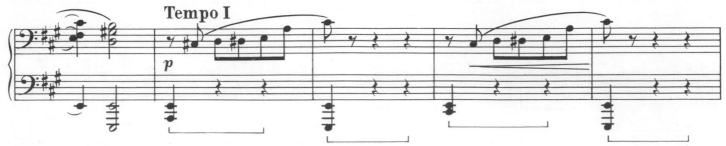

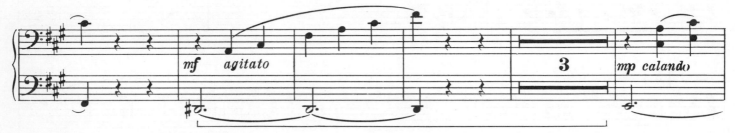

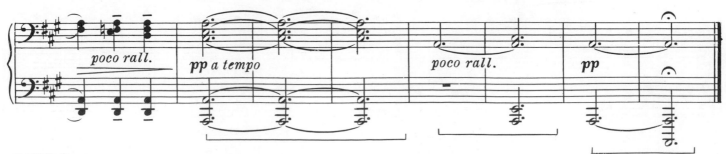

Tempo I

Birthday March
Op. 85 No. 1

Secondo

Robert Schumann
(1810 - 1856)

* Pedal is marked for both parts. Either secondo or primo may pedal.

S. M. L. 6   From Oesterle's *Graded Four-Hand Collection*, copyright 1910 by G. Schirmer, Inc., reprinted by permission.

Birthday March

Op. 85 No. 1

Primo

Robert Schumann
(1810 - 1856)

Alla marcia

* Pedal is marked for both parts. Either secondo or primo may pedal.

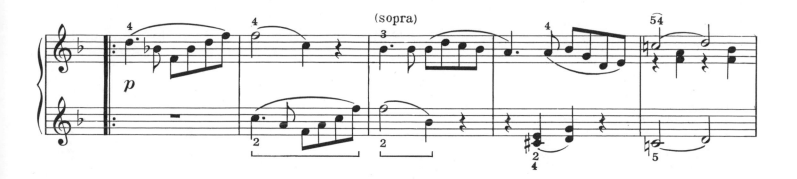

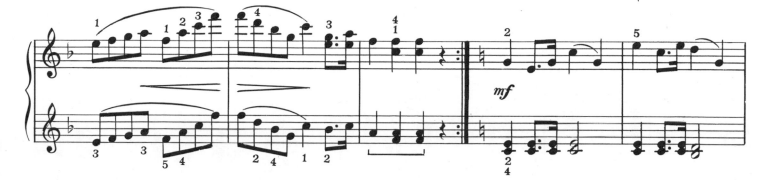

Waltz

Op. 59 No. 2

Secondo

Christian Sinding
(1856-1941)

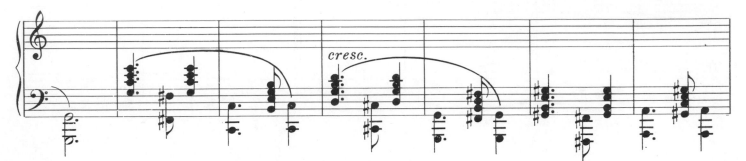

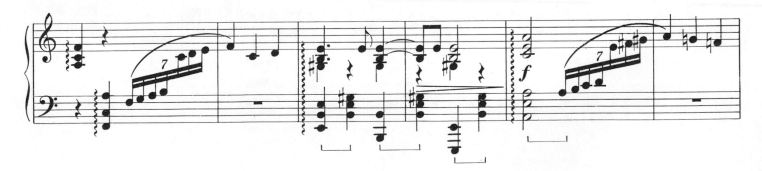

Waltz

Op. 59 No. 2

Primo

Christian Sinding
(1856–1941)

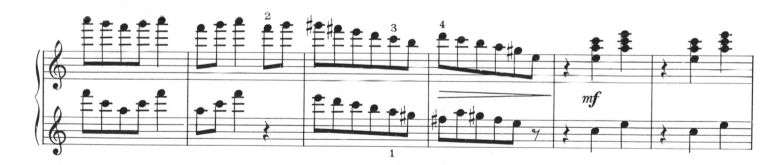

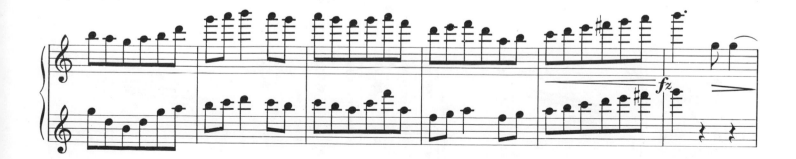

Secondo

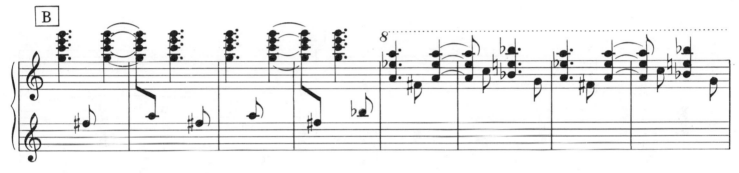

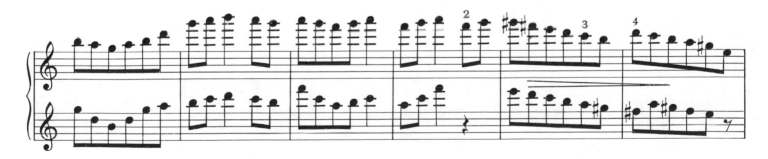

Secondo

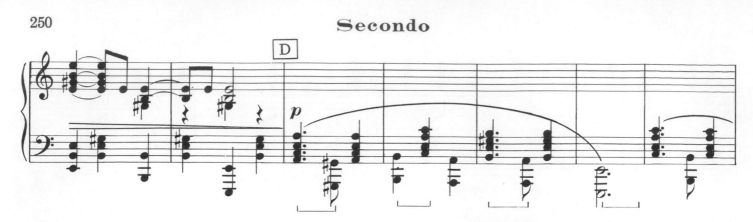

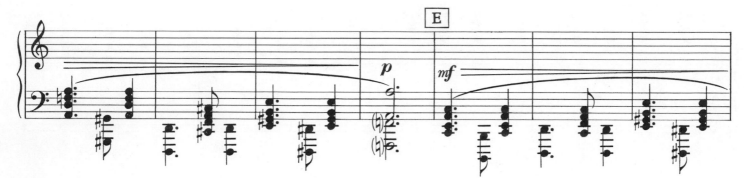

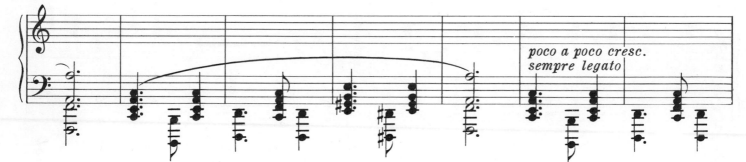

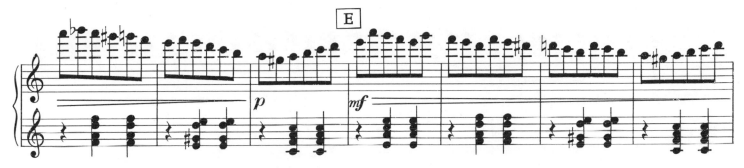

Adagio
Op. 10 No. 5

Secondo

Carl Maria von Weber
(1786 - 1826)

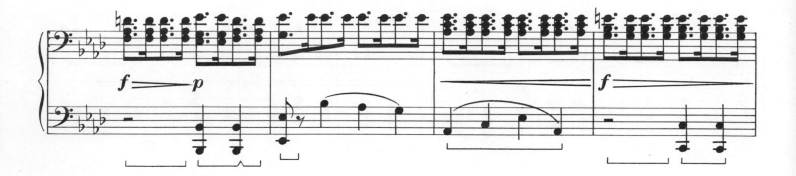

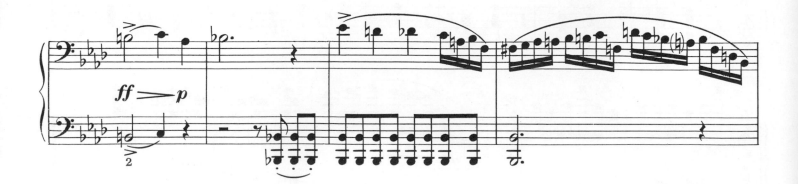

Adagio

Op. 10 No. 5

Primo

Carl Maria von Weber
(1786 - 1826)

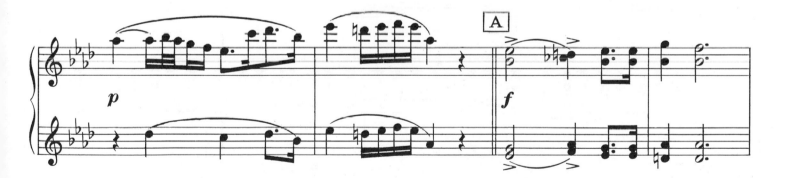

Secondo

B

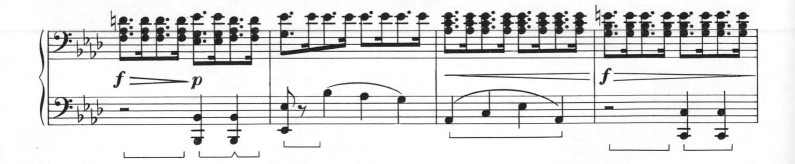

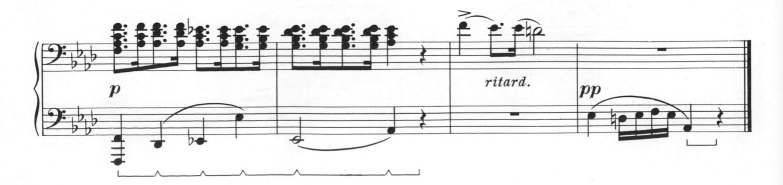

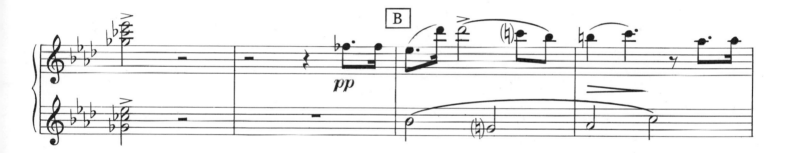